123

WE DICKINSONS

WE DICKINSONS

The life of Emily Dickinson as seen through
the eyes of her brother Austin

AILEEN FISHER & OLIVE RABE

decorations by Ellen Raskin

Atheneum   New York 1966

ACKNOWLEDGMENTS

The authors gratefully acknowledge the following permissions: Poems quoted in full: 1333, 1463, 1488, 76, 1510, 1564, 324, 12, 674, 1116; poems quoted in part: 159, 986, 1760, 817, 315, 293, 311, 668, 67, 1104, 1597, 1295, 1544, 160, 1072 from *The Poems of Emily Dickinson*, Thomas H. Johnson, Editor copyright 1958; and miscellaneous quotations from *The Letters of Emily Dickinson*, Thomas H. Johnson, Editor reprinted by permission of the publishers, Cambridge, Mass.: The Belknap Press of Harvard University Press, Copyright 1951-'55 by the President and Fellows of Harvard College, and the Trustees of Amherst College.

To Thomas H. Johnson

in appreciation of his years of dedicated work in
editing and annotating *The Poems of Emily
Dickinson* and *The Letters of Emily Dickinson.*

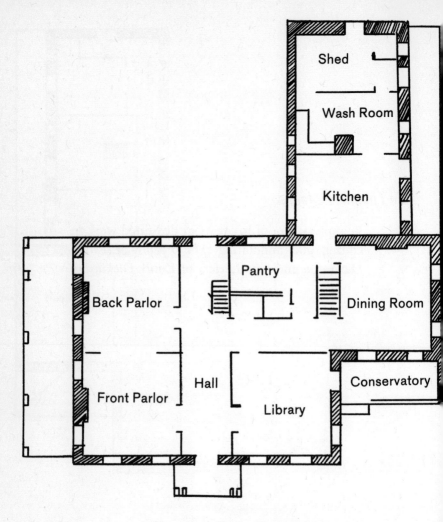

Homestead—Ground Floor

From *The Years and Hours of Emily Dickinson* by Jay Leyda, frontispiece to Vol. II: "Plan of the ground floor of the Dickinson homestead (before remodeling in 1916 by Howe & Manning, Boston)."

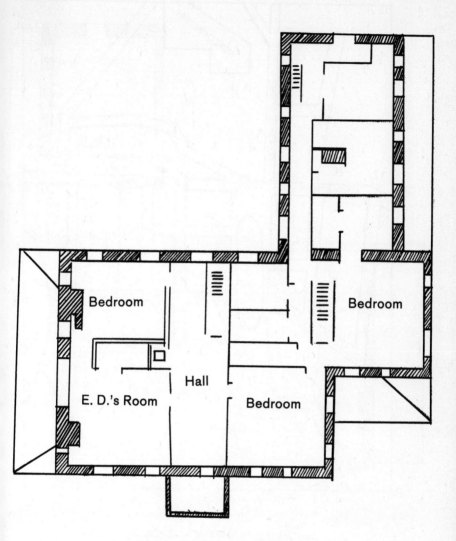

Homestead—Second Floor

From *The Years and Hours of Emily Dickinson* by Jay Leyda, frontispiece to Vol. II: "Plan of the second floor of the homestead; the third floor was an unfinished attic before remodeling."

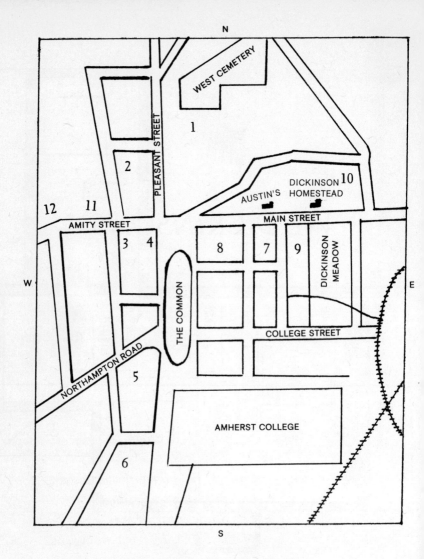

The Town Center of Amherst
(Redrawn from an atlas published in 1873.)

1. Pleasant Street Home
2. Primary School
3. Amherst Academy
4. Boltwood's Tavern, later
   Amherst House
5. Meeting House, later
   College Hall
6. Helen Hunt Jackson's
   Birthplace
7. Church and Parsonage
8. Town Hall
9. Professor Mather's Home
10. Luke Sweetser's Home
11. Professor Warner's Home
12. William Cutler's Home

WE DICKINSONS

Bred as we, among the mountains,
Can the sailor understand
The divine intoxication
Of the first league out from land?

E.D.

CHAPTER 1

SPRING—that was the season of year Emily always looked forward to most. Our long cold Massachusetts winter had a way of turning out to be too long and too cold. We had our share of fun, of course—sleigh rides, snowhouses in the drifts behind the woodpile, skating on the shallow ponds in the meadow across the road. But by March Emily was yearning for a change. She welcomed the blustery wind, no matter how cold and gray. It blew winter away and blew the birds back home. Soon we could search out arbutus in the Pelham woods and watch the fields and orchards of Amherst burst into bloom.

But the spring of 1840 was different, the spring I was

eleven years old and Emily a few months past nine. We could hardly bear to think of April coming.

Before the dreaded month arrived, though, something happened that made us forget for a while what was in store for us. A traveling artist came to Amherst, and Father decided to have portraits painted of all us Dickinsons—of himself, of Mother, and of Emily and Vinnie and me. He talked it over with Mama after his mind was already made up, knowing that she would agree.

"The three children in one picture, with Austin in the middle since he's tallest—and a boy. Emily to the left, holding a book perhaps. And little Vinnie on the right."

"Yes, Edward."

"And a separate canvas for you, and one for me. I'll make it clear to Mr. Bullard. He's rented a room over Pitkin and Kellogg's store, but I prefer to have the sittings here at the homestead."

Emily and I had never seen a real artist, and we were fascinated at the thought of a picture growing, developing, on a piece of canvas. When Father was ready for the first sitting, dressed in his best black broadcloth suit and black silk stock, I asked him to let us watch while Mr. Bullard painted.

"No, Austin," he answered. "This is a matter for the sitter and the artist only. There must be no noise, no distraction. You and Emily take Vinnie to the kitchen and stay there."

But Mother didn't mind having Emily and me watch quietly from the doorway while Mr. Bullard

4

worked on her portrait in the parlor. Her eyes twinkled at us.

"She daren't smile out loud," Emily whispered, "or it might crack the canvas."

All too soon the three pictures were finished. I looked at them with awe, wondering how Mr. Bullard could put strokes of paint together to make a face. Mother looked with a pleased smile. Father frowned.

Emily spoke up. "That's Papa and Mama, all right. But the three of us look like three peas out of a pod."

"You're right, Emily!" Father exclaimed. "Mr. Bullard is not a great success with children, but I daresay it's too late now to do anything about it."

And then it was too late to do anything about April. It was just around the corner.

We'd be across the road, searching for the first marsh marigolds along the brook, or we'd be in the oak grove on the knoll behind the house, admiring the swelling buds, when Emily would turn suddenly and gaze at the homestead and say, "Father's the only one who can stop it, Austin."

"And he won't."

"This is the only house I ever lived in. I won't feel like *myself* on Pleasant Street. And I don't think Mama wants to move either. It will make so much work for her."

"She wants to do everything Father wants. You know that, Emily."

"Vinnie doesn't seem to care, does she? As long as she has her kitten . . ."

"It's Father who wants to move, and that's all that matters in our family. Vinnie doesn't count; she's only seven. And we don't count either, though we're older."

Emily looked at me, sort of pale. "Moving feels like pulling up roots inside of me."

I was used to Emily saying things like that. I shrugged. "Father says we need more room than just half a house. Besides, Deacon Mack wants the whole house for himself now. He owns it. He can do what he wants about it."

"But it *seems* like our house, doesn't it, Austin? Close as mittens. Didn't Grandfather Dickinson build it, and plant the orchard, and start the grape arbor? And didn't he live in it for years and years when Father was young, and Uncle William and Aunt Lucretia and Uncle Samuel and Aunt Catherine . . ."

"And all the rest!" I interrupted. "Yes, he did. But Grandfather Dickinson lost his money, and the homestead, too."

That would always make Emily sigh and turn away.

I couldn't remember much about our Grandfather Dickinson. I was only four years old when he lost everything and moved away from Amherst to make a fresh start out west in Ohio. That was in 1833, the year Deacon Mack took over Grandfather's big yellow brick mansion behind the hemlock hedge. People called it the mansion because it was one of the biggest and nicest houses in the village. But we Dickinsons usually called it the homestead because Grandfather built it and lived in it a long time with his nine children.

6

Grandfather died a few years after he moved to Ohio, and nobody ever said anything about his "fresh start." But the Amherst paper and the *Springfield Republican* printed things about him that Father kept with other valuable papers in the big soup tureen on the top shelf of the sideboard. After I learned to read, there was one clipping Father always had me read aloud on Grandfather's birthday. "Nobody ever did more for Amherst than the Hon. Samuel Fowler Dickinson," it said. "We would have no Academy here or College if it had not been for him." But Mama thought perhaps Grandfather had gone too far, mortgaging the homestead to raise money for Amherst College. She was glad Father could be treasurer of the College without feeling he had to refill the empty treasury from his own pocket.

Anyway, here we were, ready to be uprooted like a bed of flowers, all because Grandfather had lost his fortune and Deacon Mack owned the homestead, and the time had come when both he and Father wanted more room.

My birthday came on the sixteenth of April, and Father set moving day for the following week. That took all the fun out of having a birthday. Time crept up on us. The evening before the dreaded day, Father told us he planned to stay home from his law office to supervise the moving. Emily sent me a woebegone look. She was always pale, for her skin was the kind of white that never took color as Vinnie's and mine did. But that evening in the light of the whale-oil lamp she looked paler than ever. She knew as well as I did that with Father in charge,

7

we would be living on Pleasant Street in no time at all.

"Everything packed and ready?" Father asked, looking at Mother. "Except for the breakfast things, of course."

"Oh, I really can't say," Mama gasped. "With Mrs. Mack and others trying to help, I really can't say. But I've tried to follow your lists, Edward, the way you wrote them out." From her pocket she took some slips of paper, pinned together, and thumbed through them. "Oh, dear! I've completely overlooked the hoarding cellar. There's that last barrel of apples, the potatoes and cabbages, and all the preserves and jelly and apple butter on the shelves. The jars will all have to be wrapped in newspaper . . . and where am I going to find time?" She gave a deep sigh.

Emily spoke up. "Austin and I can wrap the jars."

"No, I'm counting on Austin wrapping something else, first thing in the morning," Father said. "And it will be a painstaking task. The legs of all the chairs and tables must be wrapped well so they won't get scratched. You can do it with strips of cloth and old newspapers, Austin. I'll take care of padding and roping the table top, since it's too big for a boy to handle."

"Wrap all those arms and legs for going such a short way!" I exclaimed. "And then unwrap them all again! Can't the men be careful, Father?"

"Even with the padding they'll have to be careful."

"You'd think we were moving to Sunderland or Northampton or South Hadley," I mumbled, "instead of just a few blocks away."

8

"We can't let any of our fine mahogany get scratched," Mama pointed out. We all knew what pride she took in keeping a gleaming shine on the claw-footed pieces, how she polished them once a week and used a soft brush on the pineapple-cut decorations.

"If Austin has to wrap arms and legs," Emily said, "I'll wrap the faces of the jars. But mayn't I have two lanterns in that dark old cellar?"

I didn't sleep much that night, the last night at the homestead. I heard the village bell tolling nine o'clock, warning people of bedtime. I heard the clock downstairs in the hall strike the half hour. Lying there in bed, I thought of all the places Emily and I knew so well that we would be leaving behind—the barn and the hayloft, the carriage house where it was fun to hide, the orchard that sagged with fruit in fall, the shortcut to the Pelham hills, the meadow across the road where we could dam the brook and make a skating pond in winter, the oaks on the knoll that were good for climbing.

When the robins and bluebirds began to sing, I slipped out of bed. My room was over the kitchen ell of the house; so I could creak down the back stairs to the scullery without disturbing the rest of the family. Out into the early morning I hurried. I could tell from the pink glow reflected on Mount Tom and the faraway Berkshires that the sun was beginning to rise. It would take some time for it to climb to the top of the Pelham hills and look down on the scattered roofs of Amherst. I wished Emily could be along.

I followed the road toward the hills. No one would

ever know that I had gone to make my private farewells. I would be back in time for morning prayers, and the family would think I had just been out to the hen house to feed the chickens.

But I hadn't counted on Father. He always liked to get up early. On moving day he was up earlier than ever. The family were waiting prayers for me when I slipped hurriedly into my place. Emily's eyes sent me a question mark that I caught but could not answer.

As usual Father read from the Bible. Night and morning, morning and night, we had Bible reading and prayers. This morning, even though I knew that Father might question me afterward about what he read, I had a hard time keeping my mind on it. He prayed longer than usual after closing the book. At the end he said: "Bless us in our new home, but let us never forget, Lord, that our real home is in Thee."

For once breakfast stuck in my throat. The hot brown bread and honey, the scrambled eggs, the apple-sauce, all tasted like moving day. Emily was having a hard time, too. She only picked at her plate.

After breakfast there was so much for all of us to do that Father forgot to cross-examine me. And that was the only good thing I could think of about moving from the homestead.

So much to do! First I lighted two lanterns and went with Emily to the hoarding cellar, carrying old copies of the *Springfield Republican*, *Northampton Courier*, and *Hampshire Gazette* for wrapping the jars. We took care not to use our old copies of *Parley's Maga-*

zine. Father had subscribed to it for us two years before, and we kept the back numbers to read over and over again. Emily looked too small and forlorn to be left alone there in the cellar, but I had all those arms and legs to wrap upstairs.

Father had hired a big wagon and two men to help move our things. Back and forth, back and forth, they went along the muddy road between Main Street and Pleasant.

"Take it easy, boys," Father said when they started carrying out the mahogany. "Mrs. Dickinson's father had that furniture sent over the hills from Monson when we were married. It survived the rough two-day trip by oxcart with hardly a scratch. Take care you don't scratch it now."

I picked up a load of smaller things that had been set aside for me to carry to the wagon. Father called after me, "Where's Emily?"

"Probably still wrapping the jars."

"Go and see. I don't like her to be down in that cold cellar too long. Help her, Austin, if she hasn't finished."

Father always wanted to know where Emily was, and *how* she was. He tried not to show any difference among us, yet he never actually scolded Emily the way he sometimes did Vinnie and me. Even after he had been most strict and stern, he and Emily could look at each other with twinkles in their eyes.

Downstairs I ran, past the stone wine cellar that was always locked. "Emily!" I called. There was no answer. In the hoarding cellar the lanterns were turned low, to save whale oil till the movers came. Father always impressed upon us how important it was not to be wasteful. Emily had finished her task—all the boxes were filled with neatly-wrapped jars. I dashed upstairs again.

"She's not there," I told Father. "She's finished."

"She's not here either, Austin. Wait till the wagon is loaded, and you and I will ferret her out."

We followed the men to the wagon, and Father directed how they should load the furniture that had been set there on the new grass. They must place the pieces just so, to make the best use of the space, and they must put old comforters around and between. The men followed Father's orders good-naturedly. They called him "Squire" and seemed pleased that he took such an interest in their work. As Father's youngest sister, our Aunt Libby, always said, he had a way with him.

I carried out the last of the small things to be fitted into the wagon.

"There you are, boys," Father said. "One more load and we Dickinsons will drive over in the carriage to our new place of residence."

We Dickinsons were two words he often used. They were like a strong cord binding us together. We Dickinsons walked to church together on Sunday morning, Father with his high beaver hat and gold-headed cane, Mother in her rustly black silk dress, with Emily and Vinnie and me walking demurely behind. We Dickinsons walked to church again on Sunday afternoon. We Dickinsons . . .

"Now, Austin," Father said as the wagon clattered away, "we must find Emily. I suspect she's in the oak grove."

"Maybe she's at Abby's," I suggested.

Abby Wood lived at her Uncle Luke Sweetser's because her mother and father were dead. She was Emily's best friend. They were the same age, and with only the yard and the oaks and the stone wall between our houses, they saw each other nearly every day. "No, Emily won't be at Sweetsers' on moving day," Father answered firmly.

We set off down the path that skirted the garden. Father stopped at the barn to make certain that everything had been moved as he ordered—the cow, the cutter and buckboard, the harness, the hay and pitchforks, the garden tools—everything except the horse and carriage for our last ride from the homestead.

As we stood inside the door in the sun-streaked gloom, waiting for our eyes to clear, Father said unexpectedly, "You aren't happy about moving, are you, Austin?"

"No, sir."

"You'll get used to Pleasant Street and like it as much as the homestead, I daresay. So will Emily, though it will take her longer." He looked at the almost empty hayloft where swallows were darting back and forth, crying shrilly in an effort to protect the building sites they had staked out. "The same swallows I knew as a boy . . . or perhaps their great-great-grandchildren several times removed. The same pigeons cooing." He sighed.

"In many ways it is harder for me to move than for you and Emily."

I looked at him in surprise. Father reluctant to move? On the surface he seemed so eager, so full of plans.

"I know it's the thing to do, and I have steeled myself to it, Austin. But this place is more home to me than it is to you. I was only ten years old when your Grandfather built the homestead and we moved in. That was twenty-seven years ago. Ever since our marriage, except for the first year or two, your mother and I have lived here. One does not easily break the habit of a quarter of a century, son."

"Then why are we moving?" I blurted out.

"I have been doing better in law and real estate lately, and I was able to buy the Pleasant Street house. A man has a satisfaction in owning the place he lives in. This matter of sharing a house and yard and stable, even with such a good friend as Deacon Mack . . ." He broke off suddenly and looked down at me. "I'm going to tell you a secret, Austin, a secret strictly for the men of the family. You will keep it to yourself. My ambition is to pay off Grandfather Dickinson's debts and rebuild the family fortunes to such an extent that the Dickinson name will shine again. And someday, God willing, I'll buy back this beautiful place."

So Father loved it, too, and thought it beautiful—the way Emily and I did!

"It will take a number of years," he went on, unrolling the future in his mind. "But someday we will be back here where we belong, owning the ground to the west of us, too, and the meadow across the road."

Father had never shared a secret with me before, and I felt suddenly grown up. When I was eight years old, he had gone away to the legislature in Boston, the way Grandfather Dickinson had done before him. Father had called me "the man of the family" when he said good-by at the stagecoach, and had added, "I'll be depending on you, Austin." But he never depended on me. He kept writing instructions from Boston. He kept telling me to be a good boy and to get in the wood and help carry the water. He even wrote that if the well got low, I should ask Deacon Mack for water from his well. As if I couldn't be trusted to think of that myself! Now, for the first time, Father was trusting me and treating me like a man.

His eyes roved around the barn. "I'm glad to see that James has left the place in good order. Now for the oak grove and Emily."

Birds were singing, and daffodils were blooming along the path to the knoll. Emily always said that daffodils bloomed early because they could catch enough sunlight in their goblets to keep themselves warm even at night.

"Look, there she is!" Father said, pointing toward a spreading oak near the stone wall where Emily and Abby had made themselves a playhouse out of boxes. Emily was sitting there, her hands in her lap, just looking.

"Come along, Emily," Father called as we walked near. "Only one more load, and we'll drive to the new house together."

15

"What have you been *doing?*" I asked.

"I wanted to look so hard I'd never forget how it was," Emily answered.

"I know," Father said with a nod. "But we're not moving to the other side of the globe, you know. Here Austin gets up at dawn to go to the hills . . ."

I gave a start. How did Father know? Had he wanted to go to the hills himself?

"And Emily tries to impress the grove on her mind. The Pelham hills aren't going to move, and I'm sure Deacon Mack won't mind, any time you want to walk over to take a look at the grove or the homestead. And he'll no doubt be glad enough for you and Abby to keep the playhouse, Emily."

Father's voice was persuasive. We stood there quietly for a moment, enjoying the oaks with the spell of April upon them. At the edge of the grove stood a chestnut tree, sunlight slanting down its red-brown trunk. A streak of sun caught Emily's hair, and I thought how alike the colors were—chestnut color. Father's hair was dark auburn, too, and mine a mop of reddish brown. It was the only way the three of us looked as if we belonged together, for my eyes were blue and theirs were golden brown. Vinnie was Mother's girl, with the same dark Norcross hair.

We started down the knoll. "I'll miss the pine tree at my bedroom window, too," Emily said. "It's so feathery, for a tree."

"You'll grow fond of the trees at the Pleasant Street house," Father said. "There aren't so many, of course, because the yard is smaller. But tall cherry trees shade the front of the house, and the orchard is in good shape."

I wished I could tell Emily that it really didn't matter too much because someday we'd be back at the homestead. Instead I said, "I'll plant a whole grove of white pines in a few years, Emily. That's what I'll do."

Suddenly we saw one of the moving men hurrying toward us. "There's been a bit of trouble, Squire," he called out.

"Trouble? What kind of trouble?"

"Wagon's mired down in a pothole, like to tipping over."

"I trusted you'd know which ruts and potholes to avoid," Father said.

"Yes, Squire. But 'twasn't my fault. We were drawing nigh the crossroads when along comes Luke Sweetser lickety-split with his new fast-stepping roan. He afrighted my team and they swerved. The left hind wheel plunked down into one of the worst potholes in Amherst."

"What about the furniture? The mahogany?" asked Father.

"Wagon's tipped so the furniture sort of slid over. But with all that good padding, I can't see it should be hurt any."

A flush of shame swept over me. I had been so sure nothing could happen to the mahogany without padding.

"We've been trying to pry the wheel out, Squire, but the wagon's too heavy with that there furniture weighting it down. It's a case of unloading or getting

17

help. And unloading in the middle of a muddy road won't be easy."

Father nodded, but I could see that his mind was somewhere else. "You say Luke Sweetser was driving a fast new roan?"

"A pretty piece of horse flesh, Squire. But too fast for my liking."

"Hmmmm," said Father.

Emily pulled at my sleeve and gave me an amused look. We knew what pride Father took in driving the fastest horse in Amherst. Deacon Sweetser was his closest rival.

"Run over to the livery stable, Austin," Father said, "and tell them to send their strongest team. And we'll not breathe a word of this to your mother. I don't want her to start worrying about the furniture."

After the last wagonload rattled through the gate that afternoon, and Father made a final round of the premises, we Dickinsons drove in the carriage to the house on Pleasant Street. With Mother holding the precious soup tureen on her lap, and Vinnie gripping her kitten, and Emily holding two pots of her choice plants, and me two of her second-choice, and Father steadying the tall glass vase between his legs, we needed only bells, Emily said, to look like the tinker man.

"But," she added, "I'm glad we're not the tinker man, because he's always on the move from town to town, and moving *once* is one time too many for me."

After supper Mama lighted the lamp in the strange,

upset parlor and brought the Bible to one of the marble-topped tables that stood without a rug under its feet. She pushed up Father's chair for the nightly reading. When he came down from checking to see that the beds were ready, he looked around.

"Where's Emily? Where's Lavinia?"

"Emily's gone to fetch Vinnie," Mama answered. "She can't find her kitten. And I'm afraid she won't sleep tonight if she doesn't find it, Edward."

Father stood up straight and tall. "No doubt the kitten has gone back to the homestead. Cats don't like to move. Austin, rummage around and find your jacket. We'll go back and have a look."

Emily appeared at the doorway, empty-handed. I could hear Vinnie crying in the shadows.

While Father and Mother were looking for his coat, I sidled up to Emily and whispered, "It's a good omen."

"What is?"

"That cat going back home."

"Why?"

"Mightn't it be an omen that *we'll* be going back sometime, too?"

CHAPTER 2

FATHER was right about about moving. After the strangeness wore off, it wasn't as terrible as Emily and I feared it would be. For the first few weeks we were so busy we had little time to get lonesome for the homestead. I was finishing the spring term at Amherst Academy, and Emily and Vinnie were going to primary school, practically across the road from the new house. In our spare time, when our chores were done, Emily and I had exploring to do.

We found a fine woods beyond the burying ground, where bloodroot and adder's-tongues grew, and clumps of red-and-yellow columbine. Emily even found a yellow lady's-slipper coming into bloom, and she could hardly believe the wonder of it. Kneeling down, she peered into the bright golden slipper. Then she looked up at me. "There's a button inside for you, Austin."

"A button!" I bent over to look just as a bumblebee decided to leave. Fortunately I was faster. "I'll donate all those buttons to *you* hereafter," I said, and we bantered back and forth.

Hardly a day passed but we found something to laugh about or "make a hurrah about," as Emily expressed it. We especially laughed when Vinnie put on one of her mimicking acts. She would take off plump Mrs. Sweetser, or talkative Uncle Joel Norcross, or bouncy Helen Fiske, and make Emily and me rock with glee. Little Vinnie could mimic anyone, even a kitten or a hen. But we had to keep a watchful eye out, lest Father catch us urging her on.

Foot by foot, Emily and I explored the grounds around the Pleasant Street house. The stable and carriage house were smaller than those at the homestead, but we had them all to ourselves instead of sharing them with Deacon Mack. Near the flower beds on the east of the house was a grape arbor that caught our fancy. The vines were just leafing out along the arched framework above a white wooden bench.

"It will be like a cool cave here in summer," Emily said, "with green jewels dangling down."

The apple orchard pleased us most, because it kept the house from edging too close to neighbors. In a way it took the place of the knoll. I could tell from the shape of the trees and the kind of bark that there would be different kinds of apples. But I couldn't tell which trees were Baldwins or Russets or Flemish Beauties or Seek-no-furthers. That would have to wait till the apples came.

Beyond the orchard lay a little meadow that Father had bought along with the house. I hoped he would let our cow graze there some of the time instead of making me drive her back and forth to the common.

"It's not big like the meadow across from the homestead," Emily said, "and there isn't a brook lined with little white birches. But it's big enough for ripples in the grass in summer."

"And there *will* be trees some day," I reminded her. "That's where I'll plant the white pines."

One thing about the Pleasant Street house made me shout with joy. The pump was in the kitchen. At the homestead I had to carry water from the barn well, in wind and rain and snow and mud. It meant a number of trips each day, even though the hired man helped on wash days and bath nights. But now that was over, and I went around exulting.

Father heard me. "Just a minute, Austin," he said. "Work never hurt anyone. May I impress upon you that self-discipline is the golden key to success? Now that you are eleven years old, you should be glad to assume more responsibility instead of being so eager to sluff off some of it." He tapped his fingers on the sideboard. "You will, of course, continue to carry in wood for the stoves and fireplaces."

I made a mental note that with a whole house to

heat instead of just a half, I would have to carry in considerably more wood.

"And since the pump is so conveniently located," Father went on, "I will delegate more garden work to you. And for a year-round chore, you may take charge of the hen house."

"But I don't know much about hens, Father."

"You'll learn. And we'll handle it on a businesslike basis. It's time you understood the value of money, Austin."

"Yes, sir." I saw Emily move like a shadow behind us. She was carrying dishes to the sideboard and not missing a word.

"We will set up an account showing the value of the chickens now on hand. You will keep a record of the cost of the feed. Each week I'll pay you a fair price for the eggs your mother uses. If you wish to increase the flock, you may do so from your earnings. I have no doubt your mother could use more eggs than we've been getting."

And so I found myself in the chicken business.

Emily was already in the table-setting and dish-drying business, though she wasn't getting paid for it. Girls had to learn all about housework and baking and making jelly and sewing and cleaning lamps—so they could keep right on doing it all their lives, whether they married or not. I was glad I was a boy.

Yes, from the beginning we were too busy on Pleasant Street to get very homesick for the mansion. All our relatives who lived roundabout suddenly wanted to come to Amherst to see the house Father had bought. Uncle William Dickinson drove over from Worcester with Cousin Willie, and they stayed almost a week. Aunt Libby came to spend several weeks. At different times some of the Norcrosses, Mama's folks, drove over from Monson. It seemed that company was always coming or going. Poor Emily had to do so much helping in the house that we had to put off our plan for a long walk in the Pelham hills.

Father was glad to have company, we could tell. He felt good about owning the big two-story, white-painted house and showing folks around. Besides, it gave him a chance to talk politics. He was campaigning for William Henry Harrison that summer. "A good substantial Whig," Father called him. "A good man to have in the White House." One night at the supper table when Uncle Joel asked how the campaign was going, Father said, "Splendidly. The Harrison roots have already struck deep, and before long we will see an abundant harvest waving in the wind."

"Oh, Papa!" Emily exclaimed, looking at him proudly. "You sound just like the words in a book."

Then there was all the excitement over the new minister, and that kept us busy for weeks. After our old minister died, even before we moved from the homestead, the First Congregational Church of Amherst was trying out ministers, and Father was on the committee.

One day he brought a new prospect to have tea with us, a Rev. Colton from Andover. Emily and I liked him right away. He was young and nice-looking and easy to talk to. On two different Sundays he preached trial sermons, and we didn't feel like going to sleep.

Because Father was on the committee, he took his turn introducing Mr. Colton to families in the parish. When his turn was over, Father slumped in his chair after supper and gave a loud sigh.

Mother looked at him anxiously. "Are you ill, Edward?"

"No, no. Only worn to a frazzle, my dear. That Colton is a wonder! In one week he visited two hundred families and patted all the babies on the head. He wore out seven committeemen, including me."

"Then he is to be our new minister?" asked Mother.

"He's as good as installed already," Father replied, reaching for the *Springfield Republican*.

We all went to the examination at the church before the ordination. Mr. Colton stood up and answered questions for nearly two hours. Most of them Emily and I couldn't understand, but we liked the way he spoke right out when he answered.

The next day at the ordination Dr. Humphrey, president of the College, talked to the congregation first. For one thing, he told us how to act when the new preacher came to call. "Don't apologize for the looks of the house," he said. "Don't disturb the dust. Just make everything so pleasant that the pastor will want to come again soon."

At the end of the service, when the time came for hymn singing, Josiah Ayres struck up the tune on the bass viol. That bass viol! It was the only musical instrument the parish owned, and Josiah Ayres was the only one who could play it. It sounded terrible to me. I thought so the first time I heard it the year before, and I still thought so. Emily did, too. She called it the bass *vile*.

After the ordination Father stopped at his office on the way home, and we went on without him. When we got home, Mama went upstairs to change her dress. That gave Emily a chance to shake her finger at me and say, "Austin, when the pastor comes to call, don't disturb the dust!"

"I'll write my name in it instead," I answered.

Vinnie piped up. "What does it mean—not to disturb the dust?"

"It means to hide the dustcloth and not bother about polishing the furniture," Emily answered. "You know how Mama always fusses over cleaning the house when she knows company is coming. Well, Dr. Humphrey doesn't believe in women getting so tired they can't enjoy the minister."

Vinnie stood up before us the way Dr. Humphrey had and put on his voice. "When the pastor comes to call," she said, "write his name on the mahogany. Give him gingerbread and custard pie, so he can't stay away."

Emily and I hooted.

"And now," I said, "we will close the service with some music on the bass vile." I ran for an umbrella from the umbrella stand and began to saw across it with Father's second-best cane, while making the worst screeches I could. Vinnie joined me. Emily beat time.

Just as our music reached its wildest, in walked Father. "Austin! Lavinia! Emily! *What* are you doing?"

We stopped so suddenly it was like the stillness after a firecracker explosion. We looked at Father in shocked silence.

Emily spoke up. "We were just playing the bass viol, Papa. Like Mr. Ayres in church."

"The bass viol! Making fun of what happens in church? Where is your mother?"

"Here I am." Mother hurried into the parlor. "What is it, Edward?"

"Nothing less than our three children showing disrespect to the church. They were mimicking the bass viol."

I saw Mother's mouth twitch. She was holding back a smile.

"They must be punished for their transgressions," Father went on, somewhat subdued by the expression on Mama's face. I had to bring him the smaller of our Bibles, and he turned to Ezekiel and told me to write out two verses on repentance twenty-five times. Emily had to copy something from Matthew on repentance. And Vinnie had to go into the dining room and recite the Lord's Prayer and the Ten Commandments.

The next time we played "base vile," we did it out in the barn with the doors closed, when Father was attending court in Northampton. But even so he was on our minds. Right in the middle of the concert Emily stopped beating time and said, "I feel sorry for Father. He never makes a hurrah. He never has any fun."

27

I agreed with her, but with a reservation I couldn't talk about. Maybe buying a house and taking care of a family were Father's kind of fun—and working to pay off Grandfather Dickinson's debts, and dreaming of the homestead belonging to the Dickinson's again someday.

When fall came and Father suggested that Emily was old enough to go to the Academy, she shrank back. "Oh, Papa, I couldn't go without Vinnie. I'd be frightened with all those strange scholars around. Austin says there are more than a *hundred* at the Academy."

"Austin will be there to take you under his wing. And Abby Wood and Helen Fiske. It isn't as if you didn't know anyone, Emily."

"There's nothing to be afraid of," I assured her. "Of course, you'll be in the girls' section, but I'll show you around and you'll soon get to know everyone in your class."

Emily studied the tablecloth. We were eating breakfast, and she hadn't touched a thing on her plate since Father mentioned the Academy. Then suddenly she screwed up courage to face Father again. "I've been teaching Vinnie to read from my books, and she's always been better in arithmetic, and she's almost eight years old."

"Well . . ." Father looked across the table at Mother. She nodded. "We might try sending the two of you together then. If Vinnie can't keep up, she can go back to primary school for another year. By that time you will feel at home in the Academy, Emily."

"Oh, thank you, Father." The scared look smoothed

out of Emily's face. She picked up a piece of brown bread.

We didn't have to walk far to get to the Academy—just south on Pleasant Street to the business section and then west on Amity. It was a three-story brick building —older than the college—whitewashed, with Academy Hall on the third floor. Every Wednesday afternoon all the scholars, boys and girls, met in the Hall for rhetorical exercises and took turns reciting and speaking pieces. I knew Emily would dread it when her turn came.

Vinnie always made friends quickly. It wasn't long before she and, through her, Emily knew all the girls in the first-year English course. And once Emily made friends, she kept them close and sure.

When Father gave her a dictionary, she beamed. "Now that I have a lexicon, I have everything, Papa!" she exclaimed. "If I don't grow up to be a credit to you, it's because my head is screwed on wrong."

Emily suffered when her turn came to read a composition in Academy Hall on a Wednesday afternoon. She seemed so small and timid standing there in front of us. Once she started reading, though, she lost herself in the words. I looked around. Boys and girls alike were listening intently, which was more than they did when some of the rest of us took our turns. I wished Father could be there to see. When Emily finished, she ran to her seat like a bird. A little later she was laughing with the rest of us at a boy reading an amusing composition.

As election time approached, Father predicted that Mr. Harrison would get nearly three times as many

electoral votes as Mr. Van Buren, the Democratic candi-
date. But it turned out that Mr. Harrison got nearly
four times as many. "At least, I was wrong on the right
side," Father said with a twinkle in his eye.

"And that's the right side for a Whig to be wrong
on," Emily added quickly.

Mr. Harrison was inaugurated in March, 1841. At
that time there were twenty-six states in the Union. Even
Vinnie could recite the names of all twenty-six in the
order of their admission to the Union, beginning with
Delaware and ending with Michigan.

Poor Mr. Harrison never had a chance to show what
kind of President he would have made. A month after
his inauguration he died of pneumonia.

Father couldn't hide how upset he felt. He paced the
floor after supper the night he heard the news. Then
he started for the hall. "I think I'll walk down to the
office for a while," he told Mother. "Some of my friends
may want to drop in and talk."

Mother took up her workbasket. "I sometimes wish
I understood more about politics," she said to us. "It
means so much to your father. But it seems I have so
many other things to keep me busy."

One of the things Mother was busy with that spring
was the Women's Fair which the ladies of the parish
were putting on to raise money for painting the church
and carpeting the aisles. They planned to sell needlework
mainly, and Mother worked feverishly over her em-
broidery and hemstitching. She even had Emily and
Vinnie making samplers, though Emily never cared a

fig about sewing.

The fair was scheduled for late May in the hall over Mr. Sweetser's store. On the Saturday morning before the big event Mother said to me, "We want the hall to look splendid with evergreens and wildflowers, Austin, and we're counting on you and Ned Hitchcock to help gather them. Father has arranged for someone to drive you to the hills in the wagon."

"May I go, too?" Emily pleaded. "I know where the best flowers grow. I can walk straight to them, can't I, Austin? Just as if their house had a number."

Mother pointed out that Emily still had a great deal to do on her sampler. "And besides," she said, "Mrs. Fiske has been feeling poorly. I suggested that Helen come over for a while this morning to sew with you, to give her mother some peace and quiet. You know how noisy Helen can be."

I was surprised, when Ned Hitchcock came, to see that Helen Fiske was with him. They lived near each other and often played together.

"Hello, Austin!" Helen called out. "I'm going along in the wagon."

"I told her she wasn't invited," Ned said. "But she insists she's going anyway." He shrugged. "You know Helen."

Actually, neither Emily nor I knew Helen very well. She came over to play once in a while, but not often. "You're to sew samplers with Emily," I told her. "That's the plan."

"It's not *my* plan," she answered. "I'm going for

greens with you and Ned. Look, here comes the wagon! I'll beat you to it." She raced toward the road.

There was nothing for us to do but race after her and scramble into the wagon box and make the best of it.

Helen was a tomboy, but she was good fun. As it turned out, we didn't mind too much having her along. She kept telling us exciting stories that she made up. And she was good at gathering greens, too. But all the while I couldn't help thinking how different she was from my sister Emily. Emily was like a wren, full of singing; Helen was more like a blue jay.

Everyone at the fair said the festoons of evergreens and the vases of spring flowers looked beautiful. And the ladies sold enough needlework and baked goods to fix up the meeting house. Both samplers Emily made brought good prices, and she said that sort of made up for not going along to get the decorations. "*Sort* of, Austin. But not really and truly."

In the fall that year Father attended a Whig convention at Northampton, our county seat. He came home in good spirits, with a little present for each of us, but Mama waited until we were at the supper table before asking how things had gone at the convention.

"They took an unexpected turn," he answered. "At least, for me." He paused, looking more than a little pleased as he dangled his secret before us. "Two candidates were nominated for the state senate. The vote was unanimous. I . . . was one of the candidates."

"How splendid, Edward!" Mother exclaimed.

"Then will you have to go to Boston for weeks and weeks?" Emily asked. "The way you did when we lived at the homestead?"

"I'm not elected yet," Father reminded her. He took his time buttering a piece of bread. "I must say I'm much pleased with my running mate on the ticket—Samuel Williston from Easthampton." He told us how Mr. Williston and his wife had adopted four children, and how hard he had worked to support the family, farming in summer and teaching school in winter. Then his wife began covering buttons for him to sell, and the business grew and grew until they had a thousand families covering buttons for them. "Now Mr. Williston has money to promote some of his favorite projects," Father said. "He's recently started a seminary in Easthampton. It should be a good one. I plan to keep an eye on it."

Neither Emily nor I had any idea then why Father should want to keep an eye on Mr. Williston's seminary, but in due time we found out.

CHAPTER 3

A FEW DAYS before the November election we Dickinsons went back to the homestead to a big evening party at the Macks'. For weeks we had been looking forward to it as the biggest event of the season. All the faculty and officials of the College would be there, since Deacon Mack was one of the trustees.

I had been back to the homestead more than once since we moved, running errands for Mama. But Emily and Vinnie had never gone back, not even to play in the old playhouse with Abby.

The night of the party we were all excited, though Emily's excitement was somewhat tempered by her anxiety. "Things won't be the same," she said, as we

34

sat primly in the parlor in our best clothes, waiting for Mother to finish dressing.

" 'Course, they won't," Vinnie piped up. "But I want to see how *different* they are. Oh, I hope they have plenty of ice cream. Do you think the dining room will be big enough?"

"It won't be too small because of *Dickinsons* crowding into it, I hope." Mama was standing in the doorway putting on her gloves. "I trust you won't forget your manners, Vinnie."

Guests were already streaming in when we arrived shortly after seven o'clock. Soon both parlors were full of men, women, and children, and so was the wide hall that ran from the front entrance to the end of the back parlor. I heard Mr. Sweetser tell Father that more than a hundred fifty guests had been invited.

"Let's just hope they don't all come at the same time," Father replied.

Vinnie found Jane Hitchcock, from her class at the Academy, and I saw them squeeze through the crowd toward the dining room. At the end of the hall I spotted Abby Wood with Mrs. Sweetser. I pulled Emily's sleeve. "There's Abby, Emily. Follow me and I'll get you to her." I knew that Emily would feel less strange if she had Abby to talk to, off in a corner somewhere.

I made my way into the front parlor, looking for Ned Hitchcock. Father stood in the center of a group of men talking about the coming election. Since he was treasurer of the College, all the college people were supporting him for the state senate. They knew he would

35

work hard to get the legislature to vote money for the College, just as he had when he was a member of the House.

"Austin!" someone called.

It was Ned, pushing through the crowd toward me.

"Hurry! Come into the library," he said. "Mr. Sweetser and some of the others are talking about horse racing. I've been looking all over for you."

We edged near so that we could hear the racing talk. "What about it, Luke?" someone was saying. "Why don't you race Squire Dickinson with that young roan of yours?"

"Nothing I'd like better," Mr. Sweetser answered. "Trouble is, Squire Dickinson has so many irons in the fire he hasn't much time for horse racing."

Mr. Sweetser's partner in the general store, Mr. Cutler, spoke up. "I've a hunch the Squire is putting off a race till he gets himself a new horse."

The men laughed.

Suddenly we heard Deacon Mack's voice boom out from the hall. "Ladies and gentlemen, friends and neighbors!" Silence slowly settled on the crowd. "May I have your attention, please? Miss Emily Fowler has graciously consented to sing and play for us."

Ned and I were admirers of Emily Fowler. Her father was a professor at the College, and her grandfather was Noah Webster, who compiled the dictionary. She was about fifteen years old and the most popular girl at the Academy. I knew Emily and Abby would be sighing with adoration as they listened to her. How different the two

36

Emilys were! My sister would never get up and perform before a crowd of people, but Emily Fowler loved being the center of attention.

After the music Ned and I began to move toward the dining room. In the hall a group of college students and townspeople were talking to Ned's father. We stopped to listen.

"Professor Hitchcock," a young man was saying, "I understand you were a minister before you became a professor. Will you please clear up something for me? You say in your report on the geology of Massachusetts that the rocks took millions of years to form, yet the Scriptures say that God created the whole universe in six days. Which is right?"

I saw Emily and Abby edging up to the group to listen. It was exactly the kind of question Emily would want to ask.

Dr. Hitchcock had a ready answer. "We must be careful about being too literal, my friend. What did the writer of Genesis mean by a day? I have an idea he meant not twenty-four hours, but a period of time, something like what we mean by a geologic age. But whatever the period of time, the earth was created by God. Geology doesn't contradict that."

Emily was solemnly nodding her head. She thought about things like that—time and creation and God and the Scriptures. She wondered about them much more than I did, though I was more than a year and a half older. Sometimes I even thought she worried about them.

Ned gave me a nudge. "Why so solemn, Austin?

Come along. Let's see what they have to eat."

When we left the party, Vinnie confided to Emily and me that the Macks had another tub of lemonade in the kitchen and two more freezers of ice cream. "Jane and I peeked," she said. "We looked for some more of those pink-frosted cakes, but there weren't any. They were best of all."

"What did you like best, Emily?" I asked.

She was staring at the bare branches of the cherry trees against the starlit sky. "I wonder how long Rev. Colton would say the six days of creation lasted," she said dreamily.

Three days after the party at the Macks', Father and Mr. Williston were elected to the state senate. Emily was pleased because of the honor for Father, but reluctant to have him a hundred miles away in Boston for weeks on end. She even missed him when he went off to attend court for a few days at a time.

Before going to Boston, Father had something quite different up his sleeve. "I have business near Sunderland this afternoon," he said at the breakfast table the Saturday after the election. "If you'd like to come along, Austin, I'll be glad to have you." Emily looked at him eagerly, without speaking, except with her eyes. "And you, too, Emily, if your mother can spare you."

Emily and I liked nothing better than a drive in the country on a bright fall day. The road took us through woods and hills where autumn colors still lingered in the oaks and along the protected ravines. The roadside grass shone like burnished brass and rusty copper. On shadowed hillsides clumps of bare birches and aspens looked like smoke against the evergreens.

"Look at the reddish bark of the little willows there in the marsh," Emily said, pointing. "Just the color of your hair, Austin."

"What about the color of your own hair?" I retorted.

"Come, son, don't let the color of your hair inflame your temper," Father cautioned. "By the way, what color do you prefer in a horse?"

"A horse!" Emily and I exclaimed.

"It just happens that my business this afternoon has to do with a horse. A client near Sunderland, a farmer named Thompson, was in the office the other day, and he happened to mention a black mare he'd raised. Said she ought to make a good carriage horse for someone. Tom's getting old you know."

I remembered the horse talk at the Macks' party. "Is the mare fast, Father?"

"If she's as good as she sounds, she's a winner. I'd like to try her out for a week or so. You could ride her home, Austin."

"That's one way to find out if she's fast," Emily commented. "But the *best* way would be to drive past Mr. Sweetser's house sometime when he's home with his roan hitched to the hitching post."

"Now that you mention it, Emily, that may not be such a bad idea."

The mare had her good points, even though Mr. Thompson hadn't bothered to keep her groomed. Her winter hair was coming in rough and unruly. But she was strong and well built for a medium-sized horse, and she held her head like a thoroughbred. Father wouldn't have to use a checkrein on her. I could visualize her stretching out her black legs to race with Mr. Sweetser's roan.

"She'd be sleek as Mama's new satin dress if you curried her, Austin," Emily said.

We walked around admiring the mare. "She's well broke to a buggy," Mr. Thompson said, "and to a cutter in winter. And I know she's fast, though I've never raced her or timed her."

"Jump on and ride her around a bit, Austin," Father said.

I rubbed her ears and down her nose and talked to her gently before Mr. Thompson boosted me up and handed me the rope reins. The mare started off at a good brisk walk and then broke into a trot when I clucked and gave her some pressure with my heels.

"Let her go," Father called out.

I urged her on. She began to run down the field, a nice smooth fast run.

Father had Tom unhitched from the buggy when I rode back. He wanted to try the mare himself, wanted to drive her down the road a piece to get the feel of her.

"If there's anything Father likes more than a horse, it's *two* horses," Emily said as the buggy drove off.

Father came back looking pleased. "If she does that well in town, she's worth the price, Thompson."

"Why don't you try her for a week or two, Squire? 'Twouldn't put me out any at this time of year."

Emily ran to the buggy and climbed up beside Father, talking to him earnestly. I saw him nodding agreement. Then he called out to me, "I've changed my mind about you riding the mare home, Austin. I'll drive her; you ride Tom."

"Tom!"

"Don't look so crestfallen. The only way to try out the mare is to have her pull something. Emily reminded me of that open stretch in the valley where the road widens. You might let Tom run a bit there. I'm curious to see how the mare reacts to some competition."

So that was it. I grinned. Tom was getting old, but he was still fast, faster than any horse in Amherst until Luke Sweetser bought that roan. I'd be glad to race Tom against an inexperienced mare.

We went along at a trot, with the buggy in the lead, until we came to the valley. There for more than half a mile ahead the road was wide enough for us to go abreast. I gave Tom a slap on his flank and a war whoop in his ear. He plunged ahead, as if he were on springs waiting for a signal. Father slapped the reins on the mare's back, and we were off.

It was a close race, nip and tuck down the valley. But as we neared the curve where the road narrowed into the woods, Tom was breathing heavily and losing speed. The mare swept ahead, giving me her dust. Slowly Father brought her out of the run.

"Well done, Austin," he said when we stopped to talk it over. "You did your best, but Old Tom has passed his prime. And this young lady is just working into hers.

41

It looks as if she's our horse."

When we got home, Vinnie came running out to say that Abby had come to see Emily, and Mother asked her to stay for supper—and couldn't Father leave the horse hitched up so he could drive Abby home later?

No one said anything to Abby about the new mare. But Abby had bright eyes. Early the next morning, just after Father left on foot for the office, we saw Mr. Sweetser driving slowly down Pleasant Street, craning his neck toward the pasture.

It wasn't long before news of Father's new horse spread through the village. I knew that the men in the business district were wondering if the mare could beat the roan, and when Squire Dickinson and Deacon Sweetser would have their race. Emily and I hoped, of course, that the race would take place soon. But one thing after another came up and postponed any chance of it. Before we knew it, 1842 arrived and Father was off at the legislature in Boston.

The legislature adjourned early in March, but March with its mud and blustery wind is no month for horse racing. Besides, Father had something more immediate on his mind. We were all sitting around the table in the kitchen one stormy night, trying to keep warm, listening to the wind pelting the storm windows with sleet, when Father asked to see my chicken accounts. I brought him the record book. He studied it carefully and then closed the book with a nod. "You have done well, Austin. No doubt we can get William Washburn to carry on while you're away."

42

We all looked up with a start, Emily and Vinnie and I. Mama kept sewing as if she knew everything that Father was going to say.

"While I'm away?" I echoed. "What do you mean, Father?"

"Where's Austin going?" asked Vinnie.

Emily looked from Father to me and back to Father. "Not *Austin*," she gasped.

"Perhaps you remember I mentioned last fall that Mr. Williston had started a seminary in Easthampton and that I was going to keep my eye on it. It's still a small school, but it will grow, with a man like that at the head of it. I've learned to admire him more and more, working with him in the legislature. He is a man of ideals and integrity. You will benefit by contact with him, Austin."

"Do you mean I'm to go to Mr. Williston's seminary instead of the Academy?"

"Yes. At least for the spring term. Perhaps for a full year later on. I believe in boys getting away from home now and then. It will be good discipline for you to be on your own."

Emily slipped from her chair and fled like a shadow into the dining room. I knew why. She and I understood each other. She was thinking how it would be without me, and I felt hollow inside, thinking how it would be without her. It would be even worse than moving from the homestead, to be alone in a strange town at a strange school.

Father drove me to Easthampton early in April, just

43

before I turned thirteen, and enrolled me in Williston Seminary. "We will all miss you," he said when he left. "But I have no doubt Emily will keep you abreast of the news. Remember to be respectful to your instructors, Austin, and obey the rules. And I want you to take pains with your studies."

"Yes, Father," I said, struggling to keep the choke out of my voice.

By the time Emily's first letter came, I was already losing some of my loneliness. New activities kept me so busy I had little time to feel sorry for myself. But I knew that wasn't the case with Emily. Her life went on in the usual way, but with a hole in it.

"We miss you very much indeed," she wrote. "You cannot think how odd it seems without you . . . there is always such a hurrah wherever you are." She told me about the chickens, how the hens were getting along. But she lamented that the chickens would be so large I couldn't perceive them with the naked eye by the time I got home. I smiled and put the letter in my bureau drawer, vowing never to part with it.

Emily wrote me regularly. To my relief she said nothing about a horse race I might be missing. After all, I assured myself, wouldn't October be the logical time for the race, at the time of the annual Cattle Show?

When the term at the Seminary ended early in August, Father came to get me. "Gather up all your things," he said. "And say good-by to everyone. You won't be back for a while."

"Not for the fall term?" I tried to keep the glee I

felt out of my voice.

"I'll be going to Boston in a month or so when the legislature reconvenes," he replied. "I want you to enroll at the Academy again, so there will be a man in the house while I'm gone."

Though I liked Mr. Williston's seminary and my instructors and classmates, it was wonderful to be home again.

Emily fluttered around, saying, "Oh, Austin, you must see this," and "Oh, Austin, you must see that." She conducted me around the yard, and to the hen house, and to the orchard. "That tree turned out to be a Pippin, Father says, and that's an Early Harvest."

I reached for an apple. "An Early Harvest is none too early for me."

"Oh, it's good to have you home, saying things like that. Mother and Father are so *serious*. Has my face grown longer since you were away?"

I gave her an appraising look and measured her face with the knuckle of my index finger. She had always been small for her age. "Nothing about you has grown any longer that I can see, Emily."

The afternoon Abby Wood came over, we sat in the grape arbor and talked about a lot of things, including horses.

"Everyone is still wondering which horse is the faster," Abby said. "The way Uncle Luke talks, your father hasn't a chance."

"I'm sure that's what Father thinks about your Uncle Luke," Emily said with a laugh. "They both seem sort of timid about finding out, though, don't they? But now that Austin's back, we must think of a way to prod them on."

"I thought Cattle Show time would be best for a race," I said. "But Father goes to Boston to the legislature early in September. He may not be back in time. We'll have to do something *quick*."

"But what?" Abby wailed.

"I heard Mama talking to Mrs. Mack about a picnic at Sunderland the first Saturday in September," Emily remembered suddenly. "They said something about asking the Sweetsers and the Hitchcocks and Mr. Cutler and his new wife, and others. You remember that racing place on the Sunderland road, Austin . . ."

I nodded eagerly.

"Why don't you go talk to Deacon Mack?" Emily suggested. "He likes horses and he likes to arrange things. And we can keep it as secret as . . . as a muff."

Emily's idea seemed like an inspiration to me, and to Deacon Mack, too, when I sought him out. "You just let me handle all the plans," he said. "I'll see that a race comes off somehow. It's high time the question was settled."

CHAPTER 4

EMILY and I went around gleefully hugging our secret about the race until a week before the picnic. Then Father came home from a drive to Northampton in particularly good spirits. He didn't give us any explanation until we were seated at the supper table and grace had been said. Then he remarked, "I suspect Deacon Sweetser isn't feeling as contented at his supper table tonight as I am at mine."

"Is something wrong at the Sweetsers, Edward?" Mother asked.

"Perhaps *wrong* isn't the word for it. I should say *disappointing* would better cover the situation. In any event, with Seth Nims on the scene, the news will be all over Amherst by morning."

Father enjoyed making a long story out of a good one, and so we heard all about his trip to Northampton and return. On the way back he happened to meet Luke Sweetser and Seth Nims on a straight stretch of road. "What do you think they were doing?" Father asked.

"Something to do with horses," I answered, knowing that Postmaster Nims was as great a horse fancier as Mr. Sweetser.

"Were they *racing*, Papa?" Emily asked.

"No, not racing. They were clocking the roan." Father was enjoying himself. "And what could be more opportune than for me to have a chance to clock the mare? And what better way to do it than to . . ." He paused and looked across the table at me.

"Than to race with Mr. Sweetser!" I exclaimed.

"You might put it that way, Austin."

"And how did it come out?" Emily urged, as if she didn't know from the way Father was acting.

"The mare beat by a neck. And, as I said before, with Seth Nims there to clock the time, it's as official as a man could wish. I always knew that mare had it in her."

Emily and I were overjoyed, of course, that Father had won, but disappointed at the same time. It would have been so exciting to watch the race the day of the picnic. But, as it happened, some business came up, and Father wasn't able to attend the picnic anyway.

Even without the race, the picnic turned out to be exciting. Mrs. Cutler brought along her two young sisters who were visiting her, Mattie and Sue Gilbert. Sue was about Emily's age, and Mattie about mine. We had known of the Gilbert family. They had moved to Amherst ten years before, but after Mr. and Mrs. Gilbert died, the younger girls had spent most of their time away with relatives.

Emily and I were drawn to Mattie and Sue the minute Mrs. Cutler introduced them. They seemed high-spirited, and quick, and full of fun. It didn't take me long to see that Ned Hitchcock felt the same way.

One way or another, talk got around to the horse race the week before. "I suppose you would have liked to see Mr. Sweetser win the race," I said to Mattie and Sue, who were standing arm in arm, looking almost like twins in spite of their difference in age. With their sister married to Mr. Cutler, and Mr. Cutler the partner of Mr. Sweetser in the general store, it would be natural for them to want his roan to win.

Mattie nodded and smiled.

"And that's the way you feel, too?" I asked, looking at Sue.

Her black eyes flashed. "No, I can't say that it is. I don't care who the horse belongs to. I just want to see the best horse win."

I knew at that moment that Sue Gilbert was a girl I could like very much indeed. Emily felt the same way. I saw her take a step forward, as if she wanted to put her arm around Sue in spontaneous affection. Then she drew back again, her shyness of strangers winning over her impulsiveness.

Soon after Emily's thirteenth birthday in December, three things happened in a short space of time that had a profound effect on her. First, Helen Fiske's mother died. She was only thirty-eight years old, younger than our own mother.

"What will become of Helen?" Emily asked. "What does a family do without a mother? We're not like caterpillars, shutting ourselves up in our own cocoons. We need each other."

Then just a month later Emily Fowler's mother died, and again I was faced with questions I couldn't answer. "Where has she gone, Austin? Why?"

But it was the death of Sophia Holland, just a month after Mrs. Fowler's, that really shook Emily and left her weak and pale. Sophia was fifteen and in a higher class at the Academy, but Emily knew her well and admired her. When Sophia took sick with brain fever, Emily went to see her every day. She would come home and brood, her heart too full for tears. She was stunned when Sophia died.

Although Emily didn't tell anyone but me what she was grieving over, Father and Mother noticed how thin she looked, and how depressed she was. They decided a change might do her good. When they proposed sending her to Boston to visit Mama's sister, our Aunt Lavinia, Emily grasped at the suggestion.

"I never thought I'd want to go away from home," she told me. "But it's as if I've been stepping on a wobbly plank, with the sea all around me. Maybe I'll feel firmer in Boston."

With Emily gone, the house on Pleasant Street seemed suddenly cheerless and empty. I could see that Father missed Emily, too. He wrote to her often, telling her to be careful not to wet her feet or take cold, and warning her not to get lost. She brightened Father's day in a way that Vinnie and I never could. He sort of moped around, with her gone.

One morning at the breakfast table he said to Mother, "I think I will arrange to have Emily visit her Uncle William in Worcester on her way home. And don't you think it about time we suggested she leave Boston?"

"So soon, Edward? We talked of more than a month."

"With a visit in Worcester, she will be away practically a month." He tapped his fingers on the table. "Didn't Emily say something about wanting to take piano lessons?"

"She's been wanting to for a long time."

"Ever since Abby Wood started," I put in.

"I think I'll have her tell Uncle William that I want a piano, when he can get a good one at a fair price. A rosewood piano with three pedals and a stool."

I wanted to shout "hurrah" about Emily starting homeward. But would she, I wondered, feel lighthearted enough to want to play the piano?

Father's idea turned out to be a good one. Emily loved having a big square piano of her own. She began taking lessons, and life on Pleasant Street slid back to normal. Even when carrying a full course at the Academy,

51

she made it a habit to practice two hours a day. I was surprised at how fast she learned.

We Dickinsons were never particularly talented in the arts, but our interest was keen. We all liked music, though none of us ever expected to be a performer like Emily Fowler. And we all liked good books and poetry. In the soup tureen among other important papers, there was a clipping from an 1828 issue of the *New England Inquirer* signed by Father. "Wordsworth," he wrote, "is one of the few poets who will be read in the next generation. Along with the delicious melodies which he pours forth, he has *thought* on every page." Though Emily and I agreed with Father in looking up to Wordsworth, we never expected to try our hand at real poetry. The best we could do was to think up humorous valentine verses.

Somehow painting appealed to me more than music or literature. Ever since I watched Mr. Bullard paint our portraits, I had been fascinated by the ability of an artist to turn an empty canvas into a thing of color and beauty. I wondered how Father and Mother could be satisfied with those black-and-white engravings in the parlor—"The Stag at Bay" and "The Forester's Family." I was saving my chicken money to buy a real painting someday, but I never told anyone, not even Emily.

The fall I was fifteen, Father sent me back to Williston Seminary for a full year. That meant being separated from Emily again, except for vacations. But she wrote me every week without fail, and whenever I came home, we managed to slip away for walks and talks together.

She always had a new piece to play for me on the piano —a quickstep or a waltz or something sad and sentimental like "Maiden, Weep No More." She was making progress. I noticed that Father often asked her to play for him after supper, even paying her the compliment of putting down the paper while he listened.

The College faced a financial crisis that winter, and Father was worried. One week-end when I was home, I hardly saw him at all, he was so involved in meetings and conferences at the College. Then just before I had to go back to school, he came home looking relieved and relaxed.

"The College is to have a new president," he told us. "Our good friend, Dr. Hitchcock, has been named president by acclamation, and I feel our troubles are over. If anyone can pull us through this financial crisis, Dr. Hitchcock can."

I laughed. "If Ned Hitchcock's father can't get money any other way, he can figure out a chemical formula for it."

"Does he know *everything?*" Emily asked. "About mathematics and botany and mineralogy and geology and chemistry and natural history and getting money for Amherst . . . and everything?"

"Ho, Emily, you're a good one to ask that," I teased, remembering a field trip we had gone on with Dr. Hitchcock and some college and academy students at the end of the summer term. "You don't always agree with Dr. Hitchcock, as if he knew everything."

Emily looked at me in surprise.

53

"What are you saying, Austin?" Father asked.

"Well, here's the picture," I answered, gesturing dramatically. "Dr. Hitchcock takes us to a hilltop and points out the living geology and geography around us—the fertile valley of the Connecticut River, the hills and mountains encircling us, the outcroppings of stone, the swells and dips . . ."

"He explained it wonderfully," Emily interrupted. "I hung on every word."

I brushed aside her protest. "Then he calls our attention to the wonders close at hand—the trees, the flowers, in his words, 'the glorious handiwork of the Creator.' And we all take notes furiously about stamens and pistils and sepals and petals. You should see Emily observing minutely and recording her observations in her notebook."

"Of course," Father said. "It's a notebook to be proud of. Just what are you driving at, Austin?"

"She may be an attentive scholar, but she's a little rebel at the same time," I went on. "The minute she had me alone, she said she was afraid Dr. Hitchcock missed something."

"Evidence—I demand more evidence," Father said in his lawyer's voice.

"All right. First she said, 'Oh, Austin, why does science have to go and interfere?' Then she added. 'The beauty is buried under all the science.'"

Father allowed himself half a smile "Well, I can certainly appreciate Emily's feelings. Beauty *is* often overlooked in scientific analysis. But I still think Dr.

Hitchcock will make an excellent president."

Emily wore her hair done up the summer I finished my year at Williston. She was going on fifteen. Every now and then Mother made her stay out of school for a term because she thought she was studying too hard and needed exercise.

"Exercise, Austin!" Emily objected. "I can assure you I get too much of that article by staying at home. You can't imagine how much stepping around there is in a house as big as ours. If Mother only knew how much I miss school and how little I like housework! But *she* never complains, and so I try not to. Now that I'm learning to make bread, think of me with my sleeves rolled up, acquiring the most beautiful muscles."

I laughed.

"Don't laugh. There's something awesome about making bread and growing up—especially when one has a sense of guilt."

"You a sense of guilt? About what?"

She looked doleful. "I've never had the courage to tell anyone. And now that I'm practically grown up . . ." She stopped short.

"I'll never breathe your secret to a soul, I promise. What terrible sin is preying on your mind, Emily?"

She hesitated and then spoke with a breathless rush of words. "You know I never was good at arithmetic. When Father taught me to tell time on his watch—oh, it was ages ago—I didn't understand. And I was afraid to tell him I didn't. And then I was afraid to ask anyone else lest Father should find out. And so all these years

I haven't known how to read a clock. Don't laugh, Austin. Don't think poorly of your sister. But please show me how to tell time."

Poor timid Emily, burdened by such a simple guilt! In five minutes I taught her what she had been aching to know for years.

There was something else that Emily had a sense of guilt about, but it wasn't so easy to remedy. That was her feeling about religion. Like not being able to tell time, she had kept it bottled up inside of her.

One Sunday morning I found out how Emily felt. We all walked to church as usual, south on Pleasant Street, then along the open field of the common, where cows grazed and horses and buggies were hitched to a rail fence. Beyond the common the red-brick buildings of the College stood up dignified and proud above the trees; across from the common stood our yellow-painted brick church with its white belfry. We greeted friends left and right but held together as a family when we went up the steps and through the white columns of the church portico.

Sitting in our white pew with its high sides, I tried to keep my mind on the sermon. Mr. Colton was preaching on the text: "I love them that love me; and those that seek me early shall find me," and he launched into the sermon with his usual energy. I watched Emily. As long as the preacher talked about a loving God, she listened with rapt attention. But as soon as he began talking about unrepentant sinners and the tortures that awaited them in the everlasting fires of hell, I could feel her stiffen beside me.

After church, when dinner was over and the dishes washed, I found time to be alone with Emily. "Do you know I can read your backbone like a book?" I asked.

"What are you talking about, Austin?"

"When you stiffen like a ramrod, I know you're displeased."

She was surprised to learn how I had read her feelings about the sermon. "Oh, I wish Mr. Colton wouldn't talk about hell and everlasting punishment," she sighed. "God wouldn't be that cruel. Not the God I believe in."

Emily had never talked much to me about God before. Now she seemed to feel the need of it. "Sometimes when I'm alone, solemn thoughts crowd into my mind," she told me. "Don't they with you, too, Austin? I have perfect confidence in God and His promises, but I feel reluctant to give myself to Him wholly. I just can't make my peace with the kind of God the preacher talks about."

I admitted that I, too, shied away from a wrathful God.

It was a guilty secret between us. I wondered what would happen if Father asked Emily point-blank how she felt. She wouldn't lie to him. But would he understand her confession? Fortunately he never asked. He never talked about how he felt either. Twice a day he read a chapter of the Bible aloud and led us in prayers, but he never spoke his thoughts. He was very active in church affairs, on committees, and a staunch supporter financially. Yet he had never joined the church. Membership in our church was limited to those who could show evidence of conversion. Was Father, like Emily, unable to go along with everything the preacher said, unable to give himself wholly to God? What did he think, I wondered, behind the closed door of his mind? Mother had no such difficulty. She had joined the church shortly after Emily was born.

Emily studied her Bible the way she studied her dictionary—because she loved it. Words fascinated her, and the Bible used words in a way that sounded like poetry. She liked the mystery of words and phrases that could have more than one meaning, like those in the parables, with a simple story on the surface and a deeper meaning underneath. And she pored over the strange words in the book of Revelation, trying to figure out what the four horsemen stood for, and the four beasts, and the lightnings and thunderings, and the angels, and the sounding of trumpets.

I marveled at the way Emily used Bible expressions in her talk, at just the right place and time. I never could think of them. Emily would look at a bed of pansies and call them "a great crowd of witnesses," or she would come home from graduation exercises at the Academy and remark, "The fields are white with harvest."

When I entered Amherst College as a freshman in the fall of 1846, Emily was bubbling over with plans and preparations for the following autumn when she would be through at the Academy. Father, like Grandfather Dickinson before him, favored giving young women a good education. He wanted Emily and Vinnie to go away to school, as he had wanted me to go to Williston. We were lucky to have Mount Holyoke Female Seminary, one of the best and biggest seminaries for girls, only nine miles away at South Hadley. Emily wanted to go there above all.

"It's in my thoughts by day and in my dreams by night," she wrote me while I was still at Williston. "I just hope I'm not anticipating too much."

It occurred to me that perhaps she *was* anticipating too much. For a home-loving girl who called the bee, the breeze, and the butterfly her favorite companions, how would it feel to be one of several hundred strangers at Mount Holyoke? And how would she like Miss Lyon, the strong-minded, evangelistic founder and director of the Seminary?

When I asked Emily to let me see her Mount Holyoke prospectus, she handed me a well-worn copy. "Imagine," she said, "the second year after Mount Holyoke was founded, Miss Lyon had to turn away four hundred applicants. Now they have more room, and she's raised the entrance requirements, but she still has to turn away applicants. What if I can't pass the entrance examinations, Austin? I'll lose my character, won't I?"

"We aren't any of us worried about that. Just don't lose your head, that's all." I gave her a grin and went back to looking at the prospectus. My eye fell on a paragraph outlining the purposes of the school. "Look here," I cried. "One of the purposes of the Seminary is to provide mates for missionaries to foreign lands. You, the wife of a missionary! When you aren't even a converted Christian. Oh, but they'll keep working on you. I suspect you'll turn out to be as ardent as your friend Abby Wood."

"I'm not going there to learn to be a missionary's wife," Emily said stoutly. "I'm going because there are so many things I want to *know*." She hesitated, and for the first time a hint of concern crept into her voice. "How was it, Austin, the first time you went to Williston? Were you awfully, awfully lonesome?"

CHAPTER 5

EMILY had been at Mount Holyoke for two weeks when I reminded Father of his promise to let me visit her soon. I knew she would be lonesome.

"I haven't forgotten," Father said. "This coming Saturday would be a good time, I think."

Vinnie spoke up. "Mayn't I go, too, Papa? And Abby Wood? We talk about it every day. If Emily misses us half as much as we miss her . . ."

"How about having the company of two demure young ladies on the trip, Austin?" Father asked. "Time certainly wouldn't hang heavy on your hands with them sharing the buggy seat. And no doubt Emily would be delighted to see the three of you."

I nodded a bit reluctantly.

"Saturday? Day after tomorrow?" Mother fidgeted, thinking of all the presents she wanted to send Emily. "Let me see, I'll bake a cake and a pie. Vinnie, you be responsible for the gingerbread. Austin, you select some of the best apples, and the kind of peaches she loves to look at, with a rosy cheek on one side and golden on the other. And bring in some of those big purple grapes from the arbor. And, Vinnie, what about some of the chestnuts from your nutting party?"

When Father saw the big basket packed and ready on Saturday morning, he felt apologetic. "Tell Emily I have no special present to send her," he said. "But I shall be glad to give her some pecuniary assistance if she needs it."

With Vinnie and Abby chattering beside me, and Father's black mare stretching her legs on the dusty road, the nine miles to South Hadley passed quickly and pleasantly. The countryside outdid itself in beauty that bright mid-October day. Patches of color still remained in pockets on the mountain slopes.

Abby groaned and covered her eyes with her hands where the narrow road cut into the mountainside and the outer edge dropped off into rocky nothingness. But aside from that we sped merrily along, the girls offering me the best in schoolgirl entertainment. I vowed I would never again be reluctant about taking them along.

As we neared South Hadley, Vinnie spotted the Seminary at once, from the picture on Emily's prospectus. It was a large four-story brick building with a two-story portico in front, very impressive-looking for a small town.

"I should think Emily would get lost in all those rooms!" Vinnie exclaimed.

"Maybe she is sort of lost," I answered. "She's such a homebody, and so young to be off by herself, not even seventeen. I just hope she isn't so lost we won't be able to find her."

Emily was waiting for us in the visitors' parlor, a large room that seemed to be swimming in cane-bottomed chairs. As soon as she saw us in the doorway, she dropped her book and flew to us with open arms. We all began talking at once.

"Just like a flock of homesick sparrows!" Emily exclaimed in the first breathing space. She turned to me. "Did you miss me, Austin, after I sailed away over the mountain?"

"It's been like a funeral without you," I said.

Vinnie put on one of her mimicking acts to show how long-faced and doleful we had been.

"And what about *you*, Emily?" Abby asked.

"If I keep busy enough, so there isn't time to think, I don't feel so wilted. And I *was* busy enough during the three days of entrance examinations. But since then I must confess to wilting. If I didn't have Cousin Emily Norcross for my roommate, I'd be as lost as an autumn leaf." She told us about her classes and her teachers, and how hard she was studying so that she could be transferred from the junior to the middle class. "But I'm not so busy my mind doesn't fly off to Amherst every chance it gets," she added.

"I knew you'd pass your examinations without any trouble," I told her.

"Not entirely without trouble, Austin. I was trembly with suspense when each day began, and exhausted when it was over. But I didn't find the questions too difficult, though the old scholars say they were harder than ever before. You see, Miss Lyon wanted to admit only about half of the five hundred applicants; so she made the questions telling ones." Emily gave a sigh and a shrug. "I wouldn't want to go through that suspense again for all the treasure in the world."

"Don't you do anything except work and study?" Vinnie asked. "Don't you have any fun? When I go to school, I don't want to just *study* all the time."

"Oh, we do other things, too, Vin. We're allowed to go on nature walks, and sometimes groups of girls climb the mountain, and next week a menagerie is coming. Miss Lyon says we may go to see the bears and monkeys if we wish."

"If you wish!" exclaimed Vinnie. "As if everyone wouldn't want to see a menagerie."

Emily shook her head. "I'm not going. I've decided it will be more fun staying at school, enjoying the solitude."

Vinnie and Abby couldn't believe their ears, but I knew what Emily meant. She didn't need activity to have fun. She could have more pleasure alone with a good book than in a crowd looking at bears and monkeys in captivity. And she could have more enjoyment climb-

64

ing a mountain alone or with me than with a group of chattering girls.

"Oh, I had the queerest dream last night," Emily said, as if eager to change the subject. "I dreamed that Father had failed and our rye field was mortgaged to Seth Nims."

I laughed. "To Seth Nims of all people, that horse-fancying postmaster!"

"I'd be mortified to death to have our rye field mortgaged," Emily went on, "to say nothing of having it mortgaged to a Democrat." There was no missing the twinkle in her eye.

"Don't worry, Emily," I said. "Father's too good a Whig to be at the mercy of a Democrat. And he's too good a lawyer and investor and insurance man to have to mortgage his rye field. Now, if Seth Nims were half as good a postmaster as he is a Democrat . . ."

We were moaning over Seth Nims's undependable ways as a postmaster when Emily's roommate, Cousin Emily Norcross, came to join us in the visitors' parlor. She was about my age, a senior in the school. We already knew her quite well from our visits to Mama's folks in Monson over the years.

Cousin Emily brought us up to date on news of our Norcross relatives. Then she talked about Miss Lyon and the school and ended by putting a black-covered record book in my hands. "You will see from this, Austin, that Mount Holyoke fledglings don't take wing without being prepared to cope with problems of finance and economics." She smiled wryly.

65

I looked at the notebook and the careful figures marked on its pages. "What is it, Cousin Emily?"

"My account book. We have to keep a record of every cent we spend, and then on Saturdays we go over our accounts with one of the teachers. I tell you, it takes all our brain power to keep our accounts straight, doesn't it, Emily?"

"Especially if you're not good at arithmetic," Emily moaned.

"Speaking of accounts," I said, "we've brought you some things from home, Emily, that you won't have to enter in your book. Father regretted that he didn't have anything special to send, but he offers pecuniary assistance if you need it."

"Tell him I'm much obliged to him, but I don't need any *pica*uniary assistance," Emily flashed back.

"Leave it to your sister to give the quick answer," said Cousin Emily, linking her arm in Emily's. "Well, who wants to take a tour of the Seminary? And where shall we start—the recitation rooms, the library, the chapel, the dining room?"

Vinnie spoke up. "We want to see *everything*."

I begged off, knowing that all the rooms were not open to inspection by male eyes. "You go ahead, and Emily and I will catch up with you later," I suggested, eager to have a talk with Emily first.

After they left, I asked her if Miss Lyon had made a missionary out of her yet, or put her into the proper frame of mind to become a missionary's mate.

"Not yet, Austin," she said. "Actually, I'm more troubled than ever."

"How can that be?"

"Two days after I arrived, Miss Lyon gave us all a sort of examination in our 'spiritual health.' She divided us into three classes—those who were already Christians, those who had hope, and those who had no hope. You can imagine where I am."

"In the third class with the impenitents. But why look so solemn about it?"

"But it *is* solemn. Some of the girls cried when their names went down as having no hope."

"At any rate you have company. How many impenitents are there?"

"As many as ninety, about a third of the school I heard one of the teachers say. She was amazed. And you should hear Miss Lyon in her special meeting for impenitents every afternoon. She talks so fervently it's hard to resist her pleading."

"I told you she was an evangelist, remember? She has a wonderful reputation as an educator, but still she's an evangelist. Do you find yourself wavering, Emily?"

"Not exactly wavering. Troubled. Sometimes I think that Miss Lyon believes that God is good and loving and forgiving. You know, the way we both feel. Then I'm almost persuaded. But the next time she talks about an angry and vengeful God, and I slink away to remain one of the lingering bad ones."

That was the last chance we had to talk about religious pressure for some time. Emily eagerly asked for news of home and Amherst . . . and the world.

67

"You can't imagine how lost I am without Father's *Springfield Republican*," she said. "It's like living on an island in nowhere."

Then I had to make a tour of the Seminary, meet some of the girls, and talk to one of the teachers, Miss Rebecca Fiske, a sister of my good friend, Sam Fiske, at the College. And then before we knew it, it was time to take Vinnie and Abby back to Amherst.

Just before Thanksgiving I drove to Mount Holyoke again, to bring Emily and our cousin home for the holidays. Although Cousin Emily was counted among the impenitents, too, we found little chance to talk about religion. All the way to Amherst we were battered and buffeted by a cold November storm. Icy rain fell in torrents, and wind howled around the sides of the mountain. We spent most of our time trying to keep dry and comfortable.

One thing we did talk about, though, was Benjamin Newton, who had recently come to Amherst to study law in Father's office. I had written Emily about Ben, saying that she would enjoy talking to him more than to any of my college friends who called at the house.

"What's he like, Austin?" Emily asked, raising her voice above the storm.

"He's twenty seven, older than most young men entering a profession. Unfortunately his health isn't good, but he has such a lively mind and such strength of character, you soon forget about his frailty."

"He'll be in Amherst over Thanksgiving?"

I had to disappoint her. "I'm afraid he's planning

to go home to Worcester for the holiday. You'll have to wait till another time, Emily. But there'll be someone else in town you like."

"Who?"

"Sue and Mattie Gilbert are visiting the Cutlers. There'll be so many parties and activities crowded into the four days, you probably wouldn't have found time to get acquainted with Newton, anyway."

The storm slackened as we approached Amherst, and Emily cried out with joy when she saw in the rain-streaked distance the red-brick buildings of the College and the white spire of the First Parish Church. "Look! Cousin Emily, there it is. Home!" she cried. One would think she had been away for two years instead of barely two months.

We didn't have Emily with us for Christmas. None of the Protestant colleges or seminaries allowed their students to go home for the day, since Christmas celebrations were frowned on by the church. But we had Emily toward the end of January for two weeks of winter vacation. I couldn't help noticing the difference in Father. With Emily gone, his nights were spent quietly and moodily over the paper at home, or he would walk back to the office and work a few hours after supper. But with Emily home, he relaxed into affability, and night office work suddenly became less pressing. He liked nothing better than to talk to her after supper, or to have her read aloud or play the piano.

I heard him ask once if she had been lonesome.

"Yes, Father," she admitted. "I thought I would get

over it. I thought I'd sluff it off like a beetle's old jacket. But I never did."

"If you complete the year, Emily, you won't have to go back."

Emily looked at him with surprise, gratitude shining out all over her face. "Oh, thank you, Papa."

Back at the Seminary, she was lonely again. She wrote me how time went so slowly she could see his chariot wheels move by. Home, she said, had never seemed so dear to her. But she was cheered by the thought that she needn't return when her year was over.

The last week in March something happened to bring Emily home unexpectedly. A young visitor from Amherst was distressed to find that a severe cold had left Emily with a nagging cough. When we learned about it, Father said without hesitation, "She must come home at once where we can take care of her. Austin, you go fetch her tomorrow the first thing."

The weather was very cold. Mother had me take extra robes for the carriage, a soft wool shawl for Emily to tie around her head and shoulders, a bottle of cough medicine, and a pair of Father's heavy woolen socks to pull over her shoes.

For once Emily was anything but pleased to see me. She bewailed the treachery of the friend who had reported her condition, and insisted that she would not go home. "I can't bear to leave before the close of the term, Austin. I can't bear not to keep up with my class."

"There's no use rebelling," I pointed out. "Orders from headquarters."

"But I don't want to be consoled about my health by

all the old ladies in town," she wailed. "And you know what a hand Father is to give medicine."

"Come on, Emily. I daren't go home without you. Take your books along. You can keep up with your class by studying at home, and I'll be on hand to help you out if you need it."

That pacified her. She packed her books and papers and hurriedly consulted with her teachers. Then, bundled up like an Eskimo, she was not too sick to laugh at the figure she cut.

As she feared, Father was merciless in his dosing. Gradually the cough went away, and meanwhile Emily not only kept up with her Seminary work but also had what she called a "feast of reading." And she became well acquainted with Newton. Liking him and admiring his active mind, as I knew she would, she came to depend on him to direct her reading. He recommended Moore's *The Epicurean* and Longfellow's *Evangeline*, and other more serious books.

In April, Emily and I walked in the woods together, and there, half-hidden in the moss under a protecting bank, Emily found the first arbutus. "Pink and punctual," she called it as she knelt to breathe in its fragrance. By May she was back in school, and abreast of her class.

"I'm afraid there will not be many impenitents left to keep me company, Austin," she sighed when we said good-by. "Sometimes I regret I didn't give in."

"It's not too late."

"My conscience tells me that, too. But it's hard for me to give up the world. Sometime . . . sometime I must ask Newton what he thinks of God and eternity."

CHAPTER 6

Emily came home early in August, at the end of the summer term. She had completed a year's work at Mount Holyoke and passed her examinations in good style. But she was still an impenitent, with no inclination to become a missionary's wife. Although she wasn't going back to finish at Mount Holyoke, I had a feeling that her education would continue without interruption in Amherst. Newton would see to that in his calm and unofficious way. More than once he had told me how the sparkle of Emily's mind intrigued him.

She was home in time to hear me deliver a speech during Commencement Week, as one of the sophomore speakers. Unexpectedly I won second prize, a tome by

Macaulay.

"I trembled for you during the speech," Emily told me afterward, "though all I had to do was sit and listen. And when they awarded you the prize, I trembled all over again because I was so proud." She smiled as she added, "How did they know I always wanted to read Macaulay's *History of England?*"

Father was interested in politics, as usual, that autumn of 1848. In a copy of the *Express* one day Emily pounced upon the reprint of an open letter he had written to the editor of the Northampton *Courier*.

"Listen!" she cried, waving the paper at me. "Listen to this. Father's giving up his subscription to the *Courier* because the editor is supporting Mr. Van Buren instead of Mr. Taylor for President. Father beseeches the editor to repent of his errors and return to the true faith." She gave me a stern look, still gesticulating with the paper. "Austin, you will soon be old enough to vote. See to it you don't wander from the true faith, lest Father stop subscribing to you."

It was good to have Emily home again, good to have our jokes together and to talk over what we were reading and thinking. Unfortunately my studies and other activities kept me from being alone with Emily as much as I would have liked. Our house buzzed with visitors and callers. This meant added work for the girls, since Mother didn't subscribe to the "disturb no dust" theory. Once when I remarked to Vinnie that I hadn't seen much of Emily over a week-end, she replied, "When she can snatch a few minutes, she goes to her room, Austin.

73

Emily has to think. She's the only one in the family who has to think."

Newton did more than any of us to enlarge Emily's thoughts. But he had to watch his step. Father liked to be the arbiter of what Emily read, and his taste—which ran mainly to theological works—was not Newton's. After one or two experiences of coming to call with books under his arm, and having Father engage him in long-winded discussions about their worth, Newton resorted to another strategy. He hid the books intended for Emily and me in the bushes near the front door and came in empty-handed. We rescued the books later when the coast was clear.

We enjoyed the excitement of it. What if Father should discover the hiding place or, worse yet, catch Newton in the act?

"It's like living on the edge of a volcano," Emily said with reckless bravado. "We tiptoe around in a state of breathlessness, not knowing when it will erupt. Yet . . . do we choose safer ground?" She laughed and shook her head.

And then—for all the suspense over Newton—to think that I was the one to cause an eruption! I came home from College one day with a copy of Longfellow's *Kavanagh*, a new romance that was attracting considerable attention. Since the plot revolved around a young minister and two girls who fell in love with him, it hardly filled Father's requirements for proper reading matter. More than that, the book tended to satirize life in a small New England town, and small New England towns were dear to Father's heart.

He was reading the paper and Emily playing the piano when I came in with the book; so I unobtrusively slipped it under the piano cover. Later when I caught Emily's eye, I signaled to her that the book was there.

Unfortunately Father looked up at that moment. "What's this, Austin? Have you added signaling to your intellectual accomplishments?"

What could I say? The best thing to do, it seemed, was to laugh it off. "And have you, Father, added sleuthing to yours?"

"Perhaps I have." To my horror and Emily's, Father put down the paper and stood up, all six feet of him. He strode over to the big square piano. The hump under the piano cover was obvious enough. I held my breath.

"Shall I play the new piece over again?" Emily asked quickly. "Or one of your old favorites, Father?"

"Later, Emily." He put his hand on the piano cover and felt the book. "What book is this that is causing Austin so much concern?"

I could feel my face redden and my temper rise. Here we were—I, twenty years old, and Emily eighteen—being cowed by Father's censorship of our reading. Couldn't he realize that we were no longer children? Were we always to be dominated by his conservative ideas?

"It's a copy of *Kavanagh*, by Henry Wadsworth. Longfellow," I replied as steadily as I could. "It belongs to one of my fraternity brothers and has been well reviewed. I have been eager to read it, and I thought Emily would enjoy it, too."

"Let me see the book, Austin."

I took it from under the cover and handed it to him.

For fully ten minutes the three of us were silent as Father thumbed through the pages, reading a snatch here and there. Then he snapped the book shut and returned it to me. "I hardly think this is the sort of thing Emily should spend her time on. Or you either, Austin. Mind, I do not forbid you to read it. But it would please me if you returned it to its owner unread. Whatever your decision . . ." and he looked from one of us to the other, "I shall not refer to the matter again."

Emily and I both read *Kavanagh*, in the privacy of our rooms, but somehow we had little zest for it. We could feel Father scowling over our shoulders.

We read other books, too, that we knew Father would disapprove of, assuring ourselves that what he didn't know wouldn't hurt him, or us either.

Emily was quietly defiant. "I will bake his bread, make his puddings, knit his bed slippers, and entertain his guests at the Commencement tea. I will play for him, and read to him, and admire him, and love him. But I will not submit my mind to him, Austin. That is one thing it's unfair to ask of anyone. And actually, in his heart, he wouldn't want it. He takes pride in the thought that we Dickinsons are an independent breed. He knows as well as we do that our minds must be free, or we are no better than a hermit crab extruding from a snail's shell."

Emily saw a great deal of Newton that year. She shared his books with me, and his comments on authors and ideas. Her lively mind made her insatiably eager to learn. It seemed to me quite a compliment to her that an intelligent and well-read young man ten years her senior found her company so rewarding.

Emily and Newton occasionally joined the young people's crowd for social activities and outings, when they could pry themselves away from their book talk. They went along on one of the sugaring-off parties in late March, and Vinnie laughingly told me afterward that they took their scholarship with them. I was too busy with affairs of my own to notice.

Sugaring-off was one of our gayest frolics. With sleigh bells jingling, we would drive out at night to one of the wooded slopes where maple sap was being boiled in great iron kettles. When we poured the hot syrup on plates of snow, it would stiffen into candy. Most of us poured our syrup in the shape of hearts or beloved initials, but the night Emily and Newton were along, Vin reported that they poured theirs in Greek letters.

Father was not blind to the growing attachment between Emily and Newton. One Saturday morning in late July he asked me if I was free to drive to Northampton with him for the day. As soon as we were out of town, he said, "I want to talk to you about Newton, Austin. You know more about him outside the office than I do. What about the fish fry at Sunderland last week, for instance?"

"There were eighteen or twenty of us in all, Father— Emily Fowler; Sue and Mattie Gilbert; Ned Hitchcock; Abby Wood; Dan Bliss, who's new at the College and somewhat older than the rest of us; Emily; Newton; and some others. You know most of them."

"Did Emily and Newton join in the activities with the rest of you?"

I thought back. I had had enough on my mind that night without keeping an eye on Emily. Sue Gilbert, recently graduated from a female academy in Utica, New York, was back in Amherst for the summer. She struck me as more vivacious and beguiling than ever. Sue and Ned Hitchcock seemed to be hitting it off at a great rate, and I confess it made me jealous. But how could I warn Ned, my best friend, that I, too, thought Sue the most attractive girl I knew? "Well," I said slowly, "come to think of it, Father, Emily and Newton sat on a log by themselves much of the time, talking."

"Talking about what?"

"What they usually talk about—nature and books, I suppose."

"To my taste, Newton reads too widely. I'm not sure I approve of Emily being exposed to his . . . well, hardly conservative ideas. Besides, I wouldn't want her to become too much attached to Newton. Do you think she is?"

"Intellectually, perhaps. You know what an eager student she is. She always said she fell in love with her teachers, in the sense of looking up to them with overwhelming admiration. Without doubt she looks up to Newton the same way. They were probably sitting on that log at the fish fry discussing . . . immortality."

Father was silent for a few minutes. "I'm relieved to

78

hear that you think the attachment hasn't gone any further. It seems to me, now that Newton has been studying with me for nearly two years, he might be better off studying with Judge Thomas in Worcester, where Newton's family has lived for three generations. It's a much larger place. He'd have more opportunity there."

I recalled reading that Judge Thomas had recently resigned as Judge of Probate to enter into private practice in Worcester. Father was in a position to give Newton an excellent recommendation. I thought it too good an opportunity for him to miss, and Newton felt the same way when Father broached the subject to him. He decided to make the change.

When Newton left Amherst in August, I said good-by to him with some misgivings. Who could fill his place with Emily? Who would open doors for her now, show her new worlds beyond?

"Stand guard over her, Austin," Newton said when he shook my hand. "You understand her better than anyone else. You enjoy the same books . . . even the same trees, I might say. You think alike."

Newton was right. I was close to Emily, closer than I had ever been to Vin.

"Emily has a strange and wonderful mind," continued Newton. "It's like a bud beginning to open. Surely you've noticed the way she uses words, as no one has ever used them before. And with such perfect economy."

I agreed that her way of saying things often gave me a start, though I was used to expecting the unusual from her.

Again Newton urged me to guard Emily so that her time wouldn't be frittered away. "Protect her from trivia," he pleaded. "From the everlasting and endless trivia of a small town."

Before he left, he wrote in Emily's autograph album: "All can write autographs, but few paragraphs, for we are mostly no more than *names*. B. F. Newton. August, 1849." I puzzled over it when Emily showed it to me. "All can write autographs." That was true enough. "But few paragraphs." Was Newton implying that Emily was one of the few who could write paragraphs?

I knew from her early letters to me at Williston that even then she had a facility for expressing herself. Her compositions at the Academy brought praises from teachers and classmates alike. And then there were the witty pieces she contributed to *Forest Leaves*, an Academy paper, and the essays she wrote as a member of the *Unseen Trap*, an essay and social society.

"Have you shown Newton things you've written?" I asked.

She nodded. "Some compositions and some verses. I was so eager to know what he thought, Austin; so eager to know if I have any talent."

"From his autograph, I should say that he thinks so."

Emily's dark amber eyes shone in her pale face. "Will you promise never to tell? Never?" She waited for my nod and then went on breathlessly. "Newton told me I had the power to be a poet." With a gasp of anguish she lowered her eyes. "And now he has gone. Now I have only my lexicon. Oh, why must life be so full of change, Austin? He enlarged my mind, he extended my circumference."

"Perhaps it's our destiny to be led just so far and then have to go on by ourselves, Emily. Newton will certainly expect you to go on."

Looking up quickly, she exclaimed, "Yes! But it will be a lonely road without him."

It was indeed a lonely road for Emily the fall and winter after Newton left. Although I often made it a point to bring classmates home with me—Ned Hitchcock and Sam Fiske and George Gould and others—Emily seemed to be surveying the passing scene from a mountaintop. Her great new lexicon, *Webster's Unabridged Dictionary*, was her constant companion. She pored over it and delighted in discovering new words and meanings. On occasion she had animated talks with George Gould. He served on the editorial board of the *Indicator*, the College monthly, and shared Emily's interest in reading and writing. Yet sometimes she wouldn't even put in an appearance when Gould was there.

Another thing that hit Emily hard that year was Vinnie's departure for Ipswich Female Seminary in early December. Emily and Vin had always been dependent on each other, much more so than most sisters. Of course, Emily would be the last one to urge Vinnie to stay home, but the thought of being without her for months at a time was breathtaking.

Vinnie chose Ipswich over Mount Holyoke for one reason, and Father for another. Dr. Hitchcock had decided to send his daughter Jane to Ipswich and where Jane went, Vinnie wanted to go. Father favored Ipswich because it was near Salem, where his good Whig friend, Otis P. Lord, practiced law.

"It will be good to have Vinnie where the Lords can keep an eye on her," Father said.

With Vinnie gone, and me busy at College, and Newton in Worcester, and only part-time help with the heavy work, Emily was stranded in a busy household that continually demanded time and energy for what to her were trivial and unchallenging tasks.

Father, with his usual perspicacity, noticed it, too. About a month after Vinnie left, he took me aside and said wryly, "I am arranging for Emily to have some companionship. She needs it."

"There's no denying that, Father. But can one arrange another's companionship?"

"I think so, in this case. I have in mind a rather young fellow with the potentiality of growing to considerable stature."

I raised an eyebrow.

Father was obviously enjoying his secret. "I plan to introduce them tomorrow. Your mother is sure Emily will be pleased. It will tide her over until Lavinia comes back, and for a long time afterward."

The next day when I came home from College, there was no missing "the young fellow" who was to be Emily's companion. At the door Emily, her face alight, cried, "Meet Carlo, Austin! Father brought him to me. Mother insists that he can't live in the parlor, but already we have a secret understanding . . . whither I go, he goes." She stood with her hand on the head of a young Newfoundland dog.

I shouted my delight. Vinnie had her cats. Now Emily had a dog . . . and what a dog! "I can see the gentleman has the potentiality of growing to considerable stature," I remarked, mimicking Father.

From the first Emily and Carlo belonged together. He filled a place in her heart that had been waiting to be filled. The aloofness, the loneliness receded like mist in the sun. Emily improvised gay-hearted pieces on the piano and gay sentences in the silence of her room. We could hear the music, but we were unaware of the words until Valentine's Day arrived.

Meanwhile Emily had letters and a book from Newton, a beautiful copy of Emerson's *Poems*. But Carlo kept her from missing Newton too keenly. How unexpectedly good Father's timing turned out to be!

Then a humorous letter to George Gould, in the form of a prose valentine, appeared in the *Indicator*, printed anonymously. Even if he hadn't told me he was going to print it in the College paper in retaliation for Emily's sending it, I would have guessed the author from the part that read: "That's what they call a metaphor in our country. Don't be afraid of it, sir. It won't bite! If it was my *Carlo* now. The Dog is the noblest work of Art, sir. I may safely say the noblest. . . ."

I chuckled. Carlo was already acquiring stature, breaking into print in the College paper.

CHAPTER 7

When the great religious revival of 1850 swept across New England, I wondered if Emily would be caught up in it. She was then in her twentieth year. Outwardly she conformed to the family traditions of Bible reading, family prayers, and church attendance twice every Sunday, although she had her own idea of God and her own way of worship. But family traditions had nothing to do with revival meetings. They were held on weekday evenings, and our energetic Rev. Colton and impassioned preachers from other towns kept the audience spellbound, urging impenitents to repent of their sins and accept the salvation of the Lord. The meetings had a strange sort of fascination for me.

Even Vinnie off in Ipswich became infected with revival fever. She wrote fervently, "How beautiful, if *we three* could all believe in Christ, how much higher object should we have in living!" And when she and Jane Hitchcock came home in mid-March, they attended the revival meetings with zest.

The swell of religious fervor swept the College, too. It had been founded to uphold the Puritan faith after Harvard had become infected by Unitarianism. I took time from my studies to attend revival meetings, as much out of curiosity as anything else; and I was one of a group of student inquirers who met in Dr. Hitchcock's study to seek light and comfort.

Emily even had a long letter from Emily Fowler, pleading with us to seize the wondrous truth that Christ died for sinners and we were all sinners.

"I feel no impelling eagerness to seize the wondrous truth, do you, Austin?" Emily asked. "And yet I confess I often feel a desolation of spirit. Christ seems to be calling everyone right and left, but I haven't been moved to answer."

Mother went to the meetings regularly, and so did Father when he was able to be away from the office in the evening. But Emily held aloof. Father would have liked to see her attend the meetings; yet he never alluded to the subject nor suggested that she go. Even in the turmoil of emotionalism, he was true to the Dickinson motto of independence. If Emily preferred the solitude of home, alone with her books and her thoughts, that was her affair. And if I preferred to keep an open mind, that was mine, too.

"This sanctification is so strange," Emily said to me one day after talking to Sue Gilbert. "They all believe they are finding the pearl of great price—Abby and Vinnie and Emily Fowler and Jane Hitchcock and Sue. And yet they can't really tell me what the pearl stands for. Still . . . it works such a marvelous change. Haven't you noticed, Austin, how the faces of good men shine beneath their halos?"

"Oh, come, Emily," I said. "I haven't noticed any halos. But I have noticed some of the eyes." I refrained from adding that I had particularly noticed the eyes of Sue Gilbert. "And there's certainly *one* good thing to be said for the revival."

She looked at me questioningly.

"The First Parish Church has voted to sell the bass viol and buy an organ."

We both noticed a change in Father. He was more silent for one thing, more drawn into himself. He read the Bible in every spare moment, even to the neglect of the *Springfield Republican*.

As the revival went into its third month, I could see that the strain was beginning to tell on Emily. "I dare not trust myself to go, Austin," she told me, with a mixture of sadness and determination. "I am so easily excited that I might do something I'd regret later."

I knew what she meant. The meetings were thronged with people, young and old. Many who said there was nothing to religion went out of curiosity and left as converts.

Then an unexpected turn of events eased the pressure on Emily. Mother took sick. With Vinnie back in school at Ipswich, the burden of the sickroom as well as the kitchen fell on Emily. She was tied to the house from morning till night, with no time to think of revival meetings, let alone attend them.

Unfortunately she had no time for other activities either. I found her with tears in her eyes one afternoon when I came home to pick up some books I had forgotten.

"Is Mother worse?" I cried.

"It isn't Mother, Austin. And I hadn't meant anyone but Carlo to see my tears. I tried to choke them back, but it was an inglorious victory."

"What happened?"

"I was washing the noon dishes when I heard a well-known rap, and a dear friend came and asked me to ride in the woods with him. I wanted to go so much, after being cooped up for so long. But how could I leave Mother? What if she called and I failed to come to her?" Emily blinked and gave me an embarrassed smile. "I went about my work until Mother fell asleep, and then I guess I just felt sorry for myself."

Who had come to take her riding? George Gould? Sam Fiske? Or one of my other classmates? I couldn't ask; if Emily wished to tell me, she would. "He was probably as disappointed as you were," I said.

"He wanted me to come very much. Now, Austin, if you can stay a few minutes, just a few, so I can walk in the orchard with Carlo, I'll be all gathered together when

I return."

Ned Hitchcock came home from Harvard Medical
School that spring to take care of the house and the
younger children while Dr. and Mrs. Hitchcock were in
Europe for their health. I welcomed Ned with mixed
feelings. On two scores I envied him—for having the
inside track with Sue Gilbert, and for knowing what he
wanted to do with his life. A year older and a year ahead
of me in school, he had finished college the fall before
and had gone right on to Medical School. Here was I,
facing graduation in August, with no idea of what I
wanted to do. How could I blame Sue if she preferred
Ned to me?

I felt dejected over my problem, and had no one to
turn to except Emily. She would be glad to listen, I
knew. But when I sought her out one day, I found her
battling a problem of her own. All the excitement over
the revival had refired her old bafflement about death. It
was a subject I liked to avoid.

"I feel that life is short and time fleeting," she said,
"and I ought to make my peace with my maker."

"Is the revival catching up with you at last?"

"No. But the world can never fill a certain emptiness
in my heart, Austin. I must keep searching."

August was a momentous month. First of all came
Commencement week, always one of the high points of
the year not only for College students and faculty, but
also for townsfolk, alumni, and farmers and their families from the surrounding countryside. A carnival spirit
descended on staid and quiet Amherst. Crowds thronged

the streets to watch the academic procession and later to gather around the booths and tent shows on the common.

For me, Commencement week of 1850 had a special significance, since I was one of the graduates. My family was pleased that I had been elected to Phi Beta Kappa and was on the program to deliver an oration. And even though George Gould walked off with most of the graduation honors, Emily assured me that I had done very well indeed.

Father and Mother held their annual Commencement tea for faculty members, seniors, alumni, and honored guests. For days ahead of time the house on Pleasant Street was abuzz with activity and fragrant with a blend of odors coming from the kitchen. I sometimes wondered how Mother and Emily and Vin had strength enough left to appear as gracious hostesses when the event itself arrived.

Meanwhile the revival meetings continued. Emily and I noticed that Father seemed to be taking them more and more to heart. I wondered if he would yield. Would he be converted?

Emily shook her head. "He's forty-seven years old, Austin, and what you might call set in his ways. I hardly think he'll give in now. You know what it would mean . . . kneeling in public before all those people. And can't you just hear Rev. Colton cautioning him ahead of time: 'You cannot come to Christ as a *lawyer*, Squire. You must come to him as a poor sinner. You must get down on your knees and let me pray for you. Then you must pray for yourself. This is not a matter of case books and legal points, but of the *soul.*' "

Emily was wrong in one way and right in another.

At the end of one of the August revival meetings Father brought Rev. Colton home with him, and they were closeted together for some time. Then we were all called together. Rev. Colton told us that Father had decided to accept Christ and join the church, and he led us in a prayer of thanksgiving.

The next Sunday Father was one of seventy admitted to the First Parish Church; Sue Gilbert was another.

Vinnie, for all her religious outbursts, vacillated for another three months before yielding and joining the church. That left Emily and me weathering the revival without succumbing to the pressure.

Something about the revival struck me as incongruous. Here was Emily, more deeply interested in religion than most of the converts, yet she was not won over. She thought about religion; she read about it; she pondered; she asked penetrating questions. As much as she liked the preacher, his orthodox approach failed to satisfy her. She kept searching for deeper answers.

One day I called her attention to an item in the *Republican* about a new preacher in Philadelphia who was creating quite a stir—a Dr. Charles Wadsworth. "Here's a preacher whose church is besieged by eager listeners," I remarked. "He must have something unusual to offer. I wonder if our Philadelphia cousins have gone to hear him?"

Emily read the article with interest. "I must write

Cousin Eliza and urge her to tell me what Dr. Wadsworth says. Think of the Colemans being able to listen to a man like that!"

Some months later Emily told me that she had read about Dr. Wadsworth being presented with an elegant casket filled with five-dollar gold pieces. "He must touch men's souls," she commented, "or they'd never open their pocketbooks so wide. If only I could hear him sometime!"

I had a decision to make after my graduation, and it weighed on my mind. How was I to earn a living? Ned Hitchcock continued in medical school. George Gould decided to study for the ministry. Other classmates turned to business or a profession. When an opening in the small school at Sunderland was offered to me, I decided to accept it. Teaching school might be the answer to my problem.

Sunderland on the Connecticut River had always been associated in my mind with fun—buggy rides and horses, picnics and fish fries, skating parties and sleigh rides, and sugaring-off parties when the sap began to rise in spring. But I soon found that teaching school there was not at all to my my taste. I missed the mental stimulation of a college town; I missed home and Emily; and I missed Sue Gilbert. By the time the Thanksgiving holidays arrived, I knew that teaching in Sunderland was not the answer to my problem. I decided to go back to Amherst and study law in Father's office. Emily called my decision a "mighty breeze."

Though Father had suggested more than once that I

carry on the family tradition and become a lawyer, he had never pressed the matter. Yet his pleasure at having me in the office was obvious. From the first he let me in on plans for getting a railroad to come to Amherst, and I found it stimulating, even exciting.

For a long time Father had dreamed of a railroad to Amherst. Stagecoaches were becoming outmoded. He felt that a railroad would be second only to the College in putting our village on the map. He and Luke Sweetser were the moving spirits in having the line extended from Belchertown about ten miles away.

Unfortunately too few of my hours in Father's office were occupied by railroad talk. Most of the time, when I wasn't poring over tomes on legal theory, I found myself serving as a glorified office boy. The groundwork to be covered seemed endless. Was law really the profession for me?

William Howland, another student in Father's office, inadvertently fanned the embers of my doubts. He seemed to be a born lawyer. Whether his task was to collect a bill, or abstract a case, or delve into Blackstone, he had enthusiasm for it. His obvious enjoyment made me feel inadequate. He even found time to tutor at the Academy on the side.

In addition, there was Howland's active social life. And nobody knew more about his social life than we Dickinsons. He spent considerable time at our house on Pleasant Street—not to talk to me or to Father, not to court Emily, but to see Vin. She was pretty and arch, and although she had just turned eighteen and Howland was twenty-nine, their attraction for each other was obvious. At first Father seemed not to notice. He would engage Howland in long discussions when he called. But as time went on, even Father couldn't fail to notice Howland's eyes roving in Vinnie's direction.

On the surface, things went along smoothly enough the first few months when Howland came to call. But soon Father forbade Vinnie to go out with him. She could see him at home; that was to be the end of it.

High-spirited Vinnie objected, and Emily and I were aware of clandestine meetings. One day Father found out that Vinnie had gone horseback riding with her suitor. Father called her into the library that evening and kept her there a long time. She emerged in tears.

"What's wrong with a horseback ride?" I asked Emily. "Why does Father object to Howland as a suitor for Vin? He approves of his work at the office and obviously likes him."

"Howland's age may have something to do with it. He's so much older than Vinnie."

"She won't give in, will she?"

"She'll skirt disaster. Somehow she'll manage to take walks with him and ride with him. We'll just have to hope, Austin, that Father won't find out."

We both did what we could to cover up for Vin, and our little conspiracy drew the three of us closer together than ever.

That was a restless year for me. Studying law in Father's office was better than teaching at Sunderland, yet it failed to satisfy me. I kept looking for something

I couldn't find. Emily noticed my turmoil, and we talked things over. "I guess I'm just not ready to settle down," I said. "I want to see things . . . go to art galleries, to concerts, to the theater. Amherst has culture, yes. We get more than our share of lectures and serious entertainments. But compared to what New York or Boston has to offer . . ."

"Does Father know how you feel about the office?" Emily asked.

"I can't bring myself to tell him."

"Don't be impatient, Austin. A way will open."

How right she was! At the best possible time, when Father was jubilant over the legislature granting a charter to the Amherst and Belchertown Railroad, I got a letter from Uncle Joel Norcross. He was a member of the committee of Endicott School in Boston, and he wrote that there was an opening for a teacher in the boys' section. The position paid well and would give me experience which might conceivably lead to an opening later on the College faculty at home. I gasped. Boston! A made-to-order opportunity to spend a year near art galleries and the theater.

At first Father was disappointed, but I finally impressed upon him that I still had doubts about law, and that this seemed too good a chance to miss. With few misgivings I put my lawbooks back on the shelf and packed my bags for Boston. I would stay with Uncle Joel and Aunt Lavinia Norcross and my two young cousins, Loo and Fanny, until I could find quarters nearer the school. And when Emily and Vin came to visit me,

94

what a whirl I would give them!

One of Emily's first letters to me in Boston contained some surprising news. At the end of her letter she wrote: *"B.F.N. is married."*

Ben Newton married! Somehow I had never thought of the possibility. Later I learned that he had tuberculosis and had married his nurse, a woman considerably older than he. When Emily wrote again, I detected a sense of relief. With someone close to Newton to look after his health, she need no longer worry so much about him.

Shortly after my arrival in Boston a gala event took place, and I congratulated myself on my good fortune. Jennie Lind, the Swedish nightingale, was booked for a number of concerts. Knowing how enthusiastically she had been received wherever she sang, I wrote to Emily and Vinnie, urging them to come and hear her with me. But at the last minute they disappointed me.

For some reason the famous Jennie failed to thrill me. My letter to the family was highly critical. Emily answered that it took daring to combat the opinion of two civilized worlds and New York into the bargain. But, she said, she was proud of her romantic, dissenting brother, and so was Father, who all but laughed out loud over my letter.

A few weeks later when Jennie Lind sang at Northampton, the family drove through a deluge of rain to hear her. All during the concert Father sat looking mad and silly, yet amused at the same time, Emily wrote; and at the end, when the performers bowed and retired, he was glad it was over. Emily herself loved Jennie for the person she was, more than for her music, which in effect amounted to agreeing with me.

During my vacation in August, I saw a great deal of Sue. We felt closer than ever, for our separation had been bridged by an intimate exchange of letters. Sue decided to try a year of teaching, too, and when I returned to Endicott School, she left for Baltimore to teach in a private school.

Emily and Vin soon came to pay me their promised visit. I showed them my favorite pictures in the galleries and took them to the theater and places of interest I had discovered. With some pride and a sentimental bow to the lad who had saved his chicken money, I showed them a small landscape I had bought, the start of what I hoped would someday be an art collection. We crammed sight-seeing and activity into every hour I wasn't teaching. Vinnie enjoyed herself thoroughly, as she always did among strangers, but Emily remarked about the hollowness of the world. Boston and its bigness were not for her. She missed the core of quiet she had on Pleasant Street and was glad to go back to baking bread for Father and watering her plants and walking with Carlo . . . and reading her lexicon.

Off in Boston, I missed out on the excitement that stirred the village of Amherst one evening in late September, when the quiet of the countryside was suddenly disturbed by the violent ringing of a church bell. Emily wrote how everyone rushed into the street, thinking there must be a fire. Amherst was chronically plagued by fires, and a church bell was the usual signal. But this time it turned out to be a glorious spectacle of northern lights coloring the sky red, with rays of gold-pink color shooting off from a kind of sun in the center. And who rang the bell to call attention to the spectacle? None other than the staid and dignified Squire Dickinson, fearful lest some of the townsfolk might miss the wonder in the sky.

Vinnie's romance with Howland progressed while I was away in Boston. Emily wrote that he came to the house often but had to be very careful about going out with Vin. Once when they thought the coast was clear, they went riding to a neighboring town and were gone all day. What a hubbub that made in the family circle when Vinnie came home! Other times they escaped detection by the narrowest margin. Their romance reached the point where they exchanged rings, and Howland proposed marriage. But for some reason nothing came of it. Emily could never explain why, and Vinnie maintained an enigmatic silence. I wondered secretly if Father had a hand in Howland's move to Springfield soon afterward.

It was probably at Vinnie's urging that Emily wrote Howland a long humorous valentine in verse the following February and sent it to him at Springfield. He at once took it to Samuel Bowles, editor of the *Republican*, and Mr. Bowles published it anonymously, as Emily had sent it. It was her first published poem. When I saw it in the paper, I thought of the secret pleasure she must feel in reading and rereading the editor's preface:

"The hand that wrote the following amusing medley to a gentleman friend of ours, as a 'valentine,' is capable of writing very fine things, and there is certainly no presumption in entertaining a private wish that a correspondence, more direct than this, may be established between it and the *Republican*."

Emily wrote to me often, asking eager questions about what she called my "four and twenty Irish boys all in a row," although the number was nearer fifty. I didn't restrain myself from telling her how impatient I felt with them. They were an unruly lot, and I had a hard time controlling my temper. More and more it dawned on me that I was in the wrong place. Teaching irked me. Why had I thought that I could run away from myself in Boston? What was wrong with me? With the best of intentions I had failed to carry through time after time. Here I was in my early twenties, adrift, without a port in sight. I hadn't even gone ahead and planted that pine grove I had promised Emily. I vowed to do it when I got back to Amherst, if I never did another thing.

One evening when I came home from school feeling particularly discouraged, a letter from Emily was awaiting me. I pounced on it. She told me about the books she was reading and of Father's caustic comments on *Uncle Tom* and Dickens. She told me how much she enjoyed the popular *Reveries of a Bachelor*, by Ik Marvel, who took his dog "Carlo" along in his daydreams. And she brought me up to date on the Reading Club—they were discussing Hawthorne's *House of Seven Gables*, Dickens's *Bleak House*, and Longfellow's *Golden Legend*.

I put down the letter and looked out at the wintry gray sky of Boston. What fun the Reading Club had been, with all of us talking books—Howland and Emily Fowler and Sue and Mattie and Abby and Gould and Emily and Vin and the others! Emily Fowler always tried to arrange a social time afterward and sometimes, if the coast was clear, we danced. Dancing and cards were frowned upon by our Amherst elders, yet we often managed to outwit them. I smiled, remembering the time when a meeting at Abby's had come to an end, and Vinnie stood up with a mischievous gleam in her eyes. "Mind, I'm not suggesting anything," she said, "but Emily can play a wonderful new quickstep, and Father and Mother are out of town, and it isn't difficult to take up the rugs . . ." Everyone laughed, and off we trooped to Pleasant Street for a few hours of stolen dancing.

But when Mother returned the next day, almost at once she noticed that the fur rug in front of the fireplace was turned the wrong way, and we had to confess.

Those had been good days. Even the time I spent in Father's law office shone forth pleasantly in my memory compared to my present predicament of trying to teach a roomful of mischievous boys who resisted learning. I resolved to finish out the school year and return to Amherst.

With relief and determination I went back to studying law in Father's office. I managed to find time for long walks and talks and buggy rides with Sue. She sym-

99

pathized with me heartily about teaching. One year of it had been enough for her, too. Her brother Dwight had done well in the lumber business in Michigan, and her unbounded enthusiasm for opportunities out West began to rub off on me. Would I like the West? Was the end of the rainbow waiting for me out there? More and more I began to mull over the prospect of going out to look things over.

That fall I took time to plant the grove of white pines. Emily and I still thought that the best site would be just beyond the orchard near the burying ground. Whenever I could get away from the office, we went together to the Pelham hills to select the best specimens of young pines we could find.

Those were glorious fall drives to the hills. Emily's childlike delight was infectious. I found myself sloughing off my concern about the future and entering Emily's world of leaves and petals. One day as she pointed out one bright maple after another and roadsides turned scarlet with sumac and wild rosebushes, she said eagerly, "Lest we be old-fashioned, Austin, let's put a trinket on." With a bright leaf in her hair, and another in my lapel, we were children again.

We Dickinsons had cause to feel celebrative that December when Father was elected to the Congress of the United States by a large plurality. The boys of the village built a huge bonfire in honor of the occasion. The next morning Father remarked dryly that the bonfire was fine, but he noticed that his woodpile had shrunk considerably during the night.

I had been back in Father's office only six months when he surprised me by suggesting that I finish my law training at Harvard Law School as an advanced student. "A law degree from a first-class school will help establish you in practice, Austin. Your grandfather Dickinson's reputation as the best lawyer in Hampshire County was built on his Dartmouth degree."

"Then how do you account for your success, Father? After Yale, you studied law in your father's office just as I'm doing."

"True, but I still should like to see you have a law degree from Harvard. And I urge you to put in your application for the spring term, Austin."

I hesitated. The more I studied law, the better I liked it, but would it be fair to let Father put me through law school under the impression that I would join his office, and then have me decide to go West to try my luck? I told him frankly what was on my mind.

He waved aside my objection, and I was touched by the magnanimity of his answer. "Get your degree. Let other decisions come later."

Emily said it somewhat differently. "Get your degree, Austin. Then maybe you won't ever want to go away from home again."

CHAPTER 8

I LOOKED dreamily out of the window at the fading light on the Harvard campus. The rosy glow in the west behind the branching elms harmonized with the glow of my thoughts. Ever since Ned Hitchcock had surprised me with the news that he intended to marry a girl from Bridgeport, Connecticut, there had been clear sailing ahead for me as far as Sue Gilbert was concerned.

I pushed aside my lawbooks and began to write Sue a letter. "You don't know how glad I am that you and Father like each other so much, and that you are so dear to the girls. In every letter Emily speaks of it."

My life had fallen into a happy pattern, after all. How differently things had gone for Emily! A recent letter from her lay before me on my desk, with startling news staring up at me. "Oh, Austin, Newton is dead. The first of my own friends. *Pace*." Yes, I repeated—may he rest in peace.

No one, not even I, could know how severe the blow was to Emily. Remembering how affected she had been by the death of Sophia Holland, I trembled to imagine how she might feel about Newton. On my first visit to Amherst I talked to her about it.

She answered haltingly, as if unable to put her loss into words. "I wrote to him, and he wrote to me until the very end. He was such a gentle teacher, Austin. He gave me faith in myself and in my writing." She raised her arms in a characteristic gesture and then let them fall in despair. "He said he wanted to live until I became a poet. And now he is gone." Her eyes filled with tears. She waited until she could trust herself to speak again. "I'm not at rest about him. Though he often talked of God, was he willing to die? Is he with his Father in heaven? That's what I want to know more than I can say."

I tried to reassure her. But who can answer such questions

I had only one consolation, and I hoped it was a valid one for Emily's peace of mind. A new friendship was ripening that spring between her and Henry Emmons, a junior at the College. She had written me about the rides and walks they took together, how he searched out early arbutus for her, and how she had even let him read some of her poems. From what I could gather, Emmons was like Newton in many ways, though ten years younger. Emily could exchange thoughts about books and life with him. I hoped fervently that he would help fill the void left by the death of "her tutor."

But Emily never forgot Newton. Many years later, on the anniversary of his death, she wrote a poem in his memory expressing her gratitude for the world of the mind and the spirit he had opened for her.

There was another diversion in Amherst that spring that I was sure would occupy some of her attention, if only because Father was so enthusiastically involved. Tracks for the railroad were being laid from Belchertown, and day by day the line crept closer. If all went well Amherst would soon see the first passenger cars arrive at the new station. I knew what a gala occasion it would be, with speechmaking and festivities, and with Father acting as Chief Marshal of the day.

The big celebration came when excursion trains brought more than three hundred people from New London to Amherst. Emily wrote that the event passed off grandly and that nobody cared that the day was hot and dusty. She pictured Father as an old Roman general, marching around the village with New London at his heels.

Emily's growing reluctance to be with crowds kept her from attending the celebration, although she was well aware that Father would have liked her near him. Instead she watched the activities from the shelter of Professor Tyler's woods and marveled at the way the locomotive could lap the miles and lick the valley up. When she finally saw the train move off, she ran home for fear of seeing someone and having to make conversation.

That was a busy summer for the folks on Pleasant Street, with the inevitable procession of visiting relatives and friends. On top of everything else Emily had the Newmans to think about. Father's sister Mary had married Mark Newman, who ran a successful publishing business in New York. Aunt Mary and Uncle Mark died within a short time of each other, leaving a son and four young daughters. Father, as guardian of the girls, arranged to have them move to Amherst under the care of an aunt. Emily, I knew, had compassion for our orphaned cousins and did what she could for them.

In spite of the continual activity, Emily found time to send me a letter once a week. It was the next best thing to talking to her. She wrote about the progress of the pine grove; about Rev. Colton's leaving and Rev. Dwight's taking his place; about Vinnie's still mooning over Howland; about our friends, the Hollands of Springfield and their coming to spend the day; about Emmons's taking Emily on drives. Their friendship was on a purely intellectual plane, I knew. Emmons had a Susan in Hadley whom he talked about often, finding in Emily a sympathetic listener.

I was home for summer vacation during Commencement week. The day after the annual Dickinson tea, when our house and grounds swarmed with guests, the degree of Master of Arts was conferred upon me by the College. Father spoke at the Commencement dinner, and in the evening we all attended President Hitchcock's party.

Emily didn't want to go. "You know, Austin," she

105

told me, "by the time August comes and I think back upon all the company we've had—all the bread I've baked and the puddings I've made and the fruit I've bewitched into jelly—I yearn for some quiet alone in my room. It's so hard to do my reading and writing at night in summer."

I knew what she meant . . . insects swirling around the lamp chimney, moths batting out the candle flame. No wonder Emily's eyes sometimes bothered her.

In the end she went to the Commencement activities and enjoyed them. "How does it seem to be so intellectual, Austin?" she asked me on our way home from the Hitchcock party. "With an M.A. from Amherst and an LL.B. from Harvard just around the corner, I'd strut if I were you, like that iridescent old cock you used to have."

"Whatever happened, you'd be the last one to strut."

"Perhaps you're right," she murmured. "Fame is fickle. I know that without achieving it."

Thanksgiving was always my favorite holiday, but the Thanksgiving of 1853, when I was twenty-four years old, was even more favorite than usual. When I came home from Harvard for the holiday, Sue and I announced our engagement. Emily and Vin knew months before, and I am sure others in Amherst suspected it, but now at last Sue's name and mine were linked together for all to see. Unfortunately the date of our marriage had to remain indefinite, since I still had a year of law school ahead of me.

Father was in Congress in Washington that winter, a

long way from home, thinking fondly of the attractions of family life. He wrote me early in the year that he hoped we could all join him in the capital for a few weeks in the spring before Congress adjourned. I wondered if the idea would appeal to Emily. Father obviously wondered, too. He said he had written for Mother and Vinnie to come "and Emily too, if she will." But he did not insist upon it.

Emily decided to remain in Amherst. With Sue to keep her company, and Cousin John Graves, a student at the College, to tend the fires, she said she much preferred Pleasant Street to the Willard Hotel. I was sorry to miss her stimulating company. Besides, I knew she would be interested in the heated controversy in Congress over the Kansas-Nebraska Bill. Of course, she kept up on the progress of the bill in the *Republican,* but it was one thing to read about it and another to listen from the gallery of the House when the bill was being argued.

Father strongly opposed giving settlers the right to decide the slavery question for themselves. He favored the definite restrictions against slavery north of the line laid down in the Missouri Compromise. When the Kansas-Nebraska Bill passed, Father sensed that it meant the end of the Whig party, which stood strongly behind the Missouri Compromise. About twenty Congressmen met in his rooms in Washington and agreed that the only hope lay in a new party, to be called the Republican Party. Father's career as a Whig was over.

Meanwhile startling things began to happen right next door to Harvard, in Boston. I could picture Emily following with interest the case of the fugitive slave, Anthony Burns. Burns, a Baptist preacher, had run away from slavery in Virginia and made his way to Boston. There he was arrested and confined to jail in the courthouse. Boston was in an uproar. Not since the days of the Revolution had there been such excitement.

Some well-known abolitionists, among them Thomas Wentworth Higginson, decided to try to rescue Burns. They addressed a mass meeting at Faneuil Hall and led the excited crowd to the courthouse. Higginson, with several others, started to batter down the door with a heavy timber. Their plot failed, and Higginson received a deep cut in the chin when the police surged in. Burns, adjudged a fugitive, was sent back to Virginia.

All that spring Sue and I had been exchanging thoughts about religion in our letters. She kept urging me to join the church. Her conversion during the revival of 1850 had made her something of a missionary toward those she loved. She pleaded with me earnestly to give myself to the Lord, and I suspected that she tried to persuade Emily, too.

In June, when I was twenty-five, I passed the Massachusetts bar examination and the next month received my law degree from Harvard. Once again the problem of what to do with my life loomed before me. Sue kept talking up the West, quoting Horace Greeley's slogan, Go West, young man. I finally decided I must make a trip to Michigan and Illinois to look the situation over.

Emily shrank from the thought. "It might mean losing both you and Sue. How could I bear it?"

"You could come visit us."

"No. The West is too big and too far away."

"But you mustn't shut yourself up in smallness, Emily."

"I agree. No one should shut himself up in smallness. But for me, Austin, bigness must come from within, where there are no limits." With a sudden motion she shook her head as if to shake off her mood. "You must find the bigness that is best for *you*. Have you talked it over with Father?"

"Before I went to law school, I did. This isn't just a whim of mine, you know. I've been thinking about the West for some time. I'll remind Father how well Sue's brother has done in Michigan."

"There are other riches," Emily murmured, and she vanished.

I had to screw up my courage, knowing how hard it would be for Father to face the possibility of losing his only son to the lure of the West.

His answer surprised me. "I shan't try to hold you, Austin. Go out and look things over. You'll never be satisfied if you don't. But don't raise your hopes too high. Your grandfather Dickinson sought prosperity in Ohio, remember. He hoped to come back and pay off his debts, but it has fallen to me to settle them."

The unexpected death of Deacon Mack a few days later put a different complexion on my plans. Now what would happen to the homestead? Would Deacon Mack's son wish to keep the big place? Would this be Father's chance to buy it back, fulfilling the dream he had cherished for so many years? I recalled that moving day long ago when Father had confided in me. His "west" was right here in Amherst, on Main Street, at the mansion.

When I broached the subject, he gave me a frank answer. "As soon as the Mack estate is probated, I'll see about buying back the homestead. My head is full of plans for redecorating and remodeling, Austin—new wallpaper of your mother's choice in all the rooms; a new porch to the west; a library out of what used to be our parlor, with bookshelves along the north wall from floor to ceiling; a conservatory off the library, facing south, for Emily's plants. Her plants are running us out of the house now, as you know. And that land I own to the west, with the little house on it . . . I envision a big house there someday for you and Sue, if Dickinson and Dickinson become partners in law. Your dreams may not be mine, but I urge you to put mine on one side of the ledger when you see what the West has to offer."

I left in October, meeting Sue in Geneva, New York, where she was visiting her sister. Together we rode the cars to Michigan, to talk to her brother Dwight.

Amherst looked mighty good to me when I returned late in the year, leaving Sue behind with her relatives. I had tried to keep an open mind in sizing up the prospects for establishing a law practice, especially in Chicago. Pitted against the uncertainty of starting out on my own in a strange place was Father's offer of a partnership someday in his well-established practice. Pitted against the newness and rawness of the West was the satisfying intellectual atmosphere of Amherst and its nearness to galleries and theaters in New York and Boston. Yes, there *were* other riches, as Emily had reminded me, the riches of family and friends and security and congenial surroundings.

The family was at the station to greet me on the cold and forbidding day in late November when I stepped from the train, leaving the West behind me forever. Father stood tall and dignified in his beaver hat and greatcoat, with Mother clinging to his arm. Emily waited pale and expectant, Vinnie pert and full of questions. When I greeted Emily, she slipped her arm through mine.

"The prodigal has returned," she whispered.

"And sure of himself for the first time," I replied. "I'm really eager to get back to work in Father's office."

Father, with the handicap of his reputation as an inveterate Whig, lost his seat in Congress in the November election. But his term in the 33rd Congress still had some months to run. "I hope Emily and Lavinia will join me in Washington for a few weeks this winter," he wrote me. "It will ease my homesickness. Your mother prefers to stay in Amherst this time, and you will have to keep things going at the office. But I look forward to having the girls with me."

I repeated Father's words to Emily. "It's a chance you shouldn't miss," I urged, "a chance that will probably never come again."

"Vinnie has quite piqued my curiosity about the nation's capital."

"Then you'll go?"

"If I do, it won't be entirely to become acquainted

111

with Washington, Austin."

"What then?"

"A visit to the Colemans in Philadelphia before returning to Amherst would be right on our way."

I sensed that Emily had something more on her mind than just a visit with our relatives. Might it be to hear this Dr. Wadsworth we had been reading so much about? Emily was forever searching for answers to her questions about God and immortality. Perhaps Dr. Wadsworth might have something to offer. During the last week Emily hesitated about carrying through the plans for the Washington trip. She clutched at flimsy excuses. Carlo would miss her. Mother would have too much work. I would forget to look after her plants. She would feel like an embarrassed peacock in her new clothes. Then when Sue wrote that she planned to return from Michigan in February, Emily declared she would rather see "our Sue" again than the capital of the United States.

But in the end she and Vin went off on the railroad cars, leaving Mother and me to rattle around in the Pleasant Street house. I had my hands full all day at the office, and as soon as Sue was back in town, my evenings were full, too.

Eagerly I told Sue about Father's plans. I walked her up Main Street and pointed out the lots to the west of the homestead where Father wanted to build a house for us. "He says we can plan it ourselves, Sue. What do you think of an Italian villa type of house?"

"One doesn't often get such an offer as this," Sue

mused. "Would you be happy living in Amherst, Austin?"

"The point is would *you?*"

She stood looking at the mansion, the trees around it, the oaks on the knoll. Her eyes roved to the spacious plot next door with the little white house that would be removed. "Yes, I'd be happy here, with Emily and Vin right next door, and you underfoot." She smiled up at me. "Just what is an Italian villa like?"

Hour after hour we talked house plans, and I drew sketches, and spring seemed more full of promise than any spring before.

Emily wrote of the round of social activities in Washington and of excusing herself more than once on the ground of not feeling well. In early March she and Vinnie glided down the Potomac to visit Mount Vernon. Emily was awed by General Washington's house, as I knew she would be, and the short trip meant more to her than days of exposure to the social life of the capital.

When Father agreed to the Philadelphia visit, I wrote to Emily, chiding her about staying away from home so long. I threatened to make bouquets of all her plants and send them to my friends. But in spite of my warnings, she and Vinnie took their time about returning to Amherst. It was late March before they stepped off the cars. Emily's eyes shone with unusual brightness when she told me breathlessly that the trip would always be with her.

It was Vinnie who talked without restraint, as usual, taking me step by step from Willard's Hotel in Washington to the Coleman home in Philadelphia. Her one regret was that she had an attack of neuralgia in Philadelphia that curtailed her activities. "Think of it, Austin. I didn't get to hear the Rev. Wadsworth preach."

"Then I'll have to ask Emily about him."

"Oh, no! Don't mention him unless she does. And I doubt very much that she will."

"What's so private about a famous preacher, almost as famous as Henry Ward Beecher?" I demanded.

Vinnie shrugged. "It's the way he affected Emily, that's all. After hearing him preach, she made an appointment to see him in his study. Afterwards she never mentioned his name to the Colemans, and to me only in the greatest confidence."

I waited, hoping for more.

"You know how Emily has felt about Ben Newton, so concerned to know if he is with his Father in heaven. It's been preying on her mind. Well, Dr. Wadsworth seems to have been able to reassure her. They talked long about immortality, and evidently about poetry, too. He writes poetry, and Emily says that much of his sermon was poetry in prose. She was quite carried away."

"Then I'll wager he didn't preach on hell and damnation," I volunteered. "If he had, Emily would never have risen to him."

In April that year of 1855, Father's dream came true. He made a deal with Deacon Mack's son for the homestead, although other buyers were eager for a chance at the property. Now Father had a new enthusiasm to take the place of his enthusiasm for the railroad and for politics. He began remodeling at once.

Emily was delighted with the idea of a little conservatory for her plants, and she was especially delighted when Father said he was having a watering pot made for her with a long snout so that she could easily water the plants on the highest shelves. But she had regrets, too, about leaving the light, cheery house on Pleasant Street.

"One becomes so *used* to a place," she sighed. "I think I shall have to go about with a lantern, looking for myself. And what a pity to have to leave your pine grove, Austin, just when it's made such a fine start! This fall the trees will be big enough for me to hear the river in their branches."

Meanwhile I was impatient to get started on my own house. Sue agreed that it would be best to defer our marriage until our house was ready to move into. But one thing after another, not the least of which was a severe attack of malaria, put off my building plans. It was not until the end of October that I felt well enough to proceed. As if to celebrate, Father took me into full partnership with him in the office, and the next week we broke ground for the new house. Emily was concerned with every detail of the plans, and she and Sue and I spent happy hours together going over the drawings. Days were far too short, and cold weather was on the way.

When we Dickinsons moved back to the homestead around Thanksgiving, Emily and I walked around the grounds in the green-apple sunlight, as she called it.

With the added porch and conservatory and the extensive redecorating, the mansion was more than ever one of the show places of Amherst. We took the path to the knoll and walked under the oak trees that still rattled with dark leathery leaves.

"There's where Abby and I had our playhouse," Emily said.

"Childhood bliss," I commented. "And now Abby has a new Bliss."

My pun jarred Emily out of the past into the present. A few days before, Abby had married Daniel Bliss, recently ordained a missionary to Syria. They were making plans to leave Amherst as soon as possible.

"Wife of a missionary," Emily said, eyes twinkling. "And Abby never even went to Mount Holyoke!"

One by one Emily's friends were marrying and moving away. Emily Fowler had become Emily Fowler Ford of Brooklyn, New York; Helen Fiske was now Helen Hunt, wife of an Army man, living at Army posts. Emmons, after his graduation from the College, had gone away to study for the ministry, and his friendship with Emily faded.

More and more Emily began turning to friends of Father's for stimulation—the Hollands from Springfield, where Dr. Holland wrote articles and editorials for the *Republican*; Mr. Lord and his wife of Salem; and Samuel Bowles, editor of the *Republican*. Sue and I, too, enjoyed the company of these older friends, whose keen minds and intellectual background added zest to any conversation.

Sue kept urging me to join the church, and I kept earnestly searching my heart and soul. Finally, six months before our marriage, I professed my spiritual awakening and was admitted to the First Church of Christ.

"I hope you have found spiritual peace, Austin," Emily said. "Even if you haven't, it means enough to Sue to bring peace of a different kind. I, too, have prayed earnestly for enlightenment, but I still feel that God is closer to me outside the creed of a church."

"And yet you are more sincerely religious than any of us, more searching, more intuitive in your understanding."

"Some keep the Sabbath in surplice," she replied with a quaint curtsy. "I just wear my wings."

Soon after we were settled at the homestead again, Mother took sick, whether from the excitement of moving or the extra work of the big house or just general weariness. She gave in and went to bed. How could Emily and Vin handle all the work demanded of them and look after a patient besides?

I stormed to Sue about it. "Poor Emily has little enough time to read and write. And Vinnie can't manage *everything*."

"What they need is full-time help," Sue replied. "We'll need it at the villa, too. It's time the girls were relieved of some of the work. Why don't you speak to your Father about it? He's reasonable. I'd say he's more than reasonable when it comes to Emily. He'd do anything for her. He just has too many other things on his mind to think of it."

That evening I spoke to Father. He listened patiently until I finished and then smiled a trifle patronizingly. "It's not easy to find good help, Austin. But beginning tomorrow Margaret O'Brien, a strong and genial Irish girl, is moving in as full-time help. I began looking for someone at least two weeks ago."

Sue and I were married that July with the blessings of my entire family. Emily especially loved Sue and looked forward to having her live next door. As it turned out, though, she probably counted too much on Sue's companionship, although Sue ran over for a short visit nearly every day. We soon became involved in a whirl of social activity, with Emily often on the outside, reluctant to join in.

How busy Sue and I were furnishing the house to our taste! From the first, money was something of a problem. Sue had expensive tastes, and so did I when it came to pictures and horses. Although Sue had a small income from her brother in Michigan, our combined resources fell far short of satisfying our wants.

Even so, I couldn't resist buying a high-stepping gelding late that summer and driving it in the Cattle Show parade, along with Father and Luke Sweetser and Seth Nims and other horse fanciers. Father, as usual, was official host for the fair. I acted as assistant to the chief marshal. And Emily took second prize for a loaf of her rye-and-corn bread. As Sue remarked, we Dickinsons all but stole the show.

CHAPTER 9

It was the night of Emerson's lecture, a night in mid-December so fine that Sue insisted we walk to the College instead of taking the carriage. Snow still lay in the shadows from a brief storm earlier in the week, and our little town of Amherst in the hills looked serene and beautiful under the bright sky.

Sue was more swept away by the lecture than any of us. Ecstatically she walked home on Mr. Emerson's arm. Emily and Vin and I, walking behind, heard snatches of animated conversation that floated back as Sue and the sage of Concord talked about books and writers.

Emerson was, it seemed to me, at the height of his powers as a writer and lecturer. Tall and slender, with penetrating blue eyes, he made a strong impression on me, and on Emily, too, judging from her eager attention to his words.

"Sue's been looking forward to this night for a long time," I said. "To have Mr. Emerson as our overnight guest . . . well, it *is* something to look forward to, isn't it?" I pressed Emily's arm affectionately. "Remember when Newton sent you Emerson's *Poems* and how highly we thought of them, Emily?"

"Don't put it in the past tense, Austin."

Vinnie broke in. "There wasn't much to the lecture, though, was there? I expected it to be deep, but I understood every word of it. What's so penetrating about *The Beautiful in Rural Life* to devote a whole lecture to it?"

"I liked much that he said, Vinnie," Emily remonstrated. "Especially that part about crowds in the cities being somewhat mad and needing the sanity of the country."

"But there's nothing new about that," Vinnie objected.

Sue and Mr. Emerson were already moving up the walk to the Evergreens when we reached the gate. We had stopped to locate some of our favorite stars, Algol and Aldebaran and the well-known four in the great square of Pegasus. I held the gate open.

"Oh, no," Emily said, drawing back. "Not tonight, Austin."

"Come on. Sue's having only a small party, folks from the College. You know them all. We'll just sit in front of the fire and talk, or let Mr. Emerson talk." I turned to Vinnie. "How about it, Vin?"

"If Emily wants to go home, I'll go with her."

Emily hid her face in her muff for a moment, as if trying to gather courage to overcome her timidity with strangers and her awe of Mr. Emerson. "For a little while, then," she conceded, and we went through the gate.

I had duties as host and, at the same time, tried to keep an ear open to the conversation. Mr. Emerson was talking about the new *Atlantic Monthly* to Sue and a few others who arrived early. Just the month before, the first issue of the *Atlantic* had contained one of Emerson's poems. Sue was pressing him to explain how the new magazine would differ from *Harper's*, already seven years old and favorite reading matter in both Dickinson households.

"As you know," Mr. Emerson said, "*Harper's* relies mainly on serials by the popular English novelists— Dickens, Thackeray, and others. The *Atlantic*, if James Russell Lowell has his way as editor, is to be the literary magazine of this country, featuring mainly our own New England writers—Longfellow, Holmes, Whittier. . . ."

"And Emerson!" interjected Sue.

A literary magazine for New England writers! I looked to see if interest showed on Emily's face. Where was she? Neither she nor Vin was in the group around the fire. Without going to look, I knew that Emily had fled.

Emily was a law unto herself. Though Sue and I regretted having her disappear from our parties, we seldom reproached her for it. If she came over with her lantern and Carlo, as she sometimes did, to talk with the Hollands or Samuel Bowles or one of Sue's seminary friends, we were elated. Her quick wit always delighted us, her improvisations on the piano held us under a spell. As one of Sue's friends expressed it, she was a choice spirit.

Often her refusals to join us had a charm of their own. I recall one note begging off from an evening party because she had spent the afternoon making calls and had accidentally left her mind at one of the houses. "But," she pleaded, "please reserve an ottoman for my spirit."

For all her belief in the timelessness of an ever-present eternity, Emily's time was precious to her. Father sometimes failed to realize her need to conserve it. One winter morning he stopped at the Evergreens on his way to the office for a second cup of coffee, as he often did, and exclaimed as he took his seat, "That sister of yours! I am taken to task because I rap on her door in the morning lest she oversleep."

"You rap too early, Father," I protested.

Taking a slip of paper from his pocket, he passed it to Sue. "She exaggerates. Three A.M. indeed!"

Sue read the note aloud. "To my Father—to whose untiring efforts in my behalf, I am indebted for my *morning-hours*, viz.—3 A.M. to 12 P.M.—these grateful lines are inscribed by his Aff Daughter." There followed a little poetic comment on sleep which Father found very clever.

"You do your best to keep Emily up late at night and then expect her to jump up like a rooster at the break of day," I chided.

"I keep her up late? All I ask is a little music, a little reading aloud. Besides, I'm busy at the office several nights a week."

"Ah, Father Dickinson, but you buy eight volumes of Shakespeare's Complete Works!" Sue exclaimed. "Do you think that Emily can let Shakespeare sit on the shelf unread or that she will be content to read him only once? And when does she have time, except at night?"

That talk with Father made me realize that lately I hadn't been very considerate of Emily either. I had been neglecting her; long private talks together were rare. I decided to reform. And so one morning in early spring when I had a little business with a client on the Northampton road, I asked her to drive out with me. Mother's long illness had kept Emily confined to the house too much; she was glad for a temporary escape. Fortunately her garden called to her whenever the weather and her household tasks permitted. The flowers in her informal beds were always among the most beautiful in Amherst. Often before going to the office in the morning, I would look across and see Emily kneeling on an old blanket, weeding and tending her flowers while the dew still glittered on the grass. The strength of the earth seemed to pour into her and keep her spirits high.

To Emily's delight the morning of our drive danced with sunlight, and the freshness of young growing things filled the air. At her suggestion we went out of our way to drive past the pine grove on Pleasant Street.

"The pines are simply galloping toward heaven!" she exclaimed. "A pity the campus and the common can't march up here and see."

"The campus and the common are going to surprise you one of these days by some activity of their own," I answered, "now that the Ornamental Tree Association has been organized. I'm on the executive committee, and my head is full of plans. But everything takes time, you know. Especially trees."

"I hope the common won't be too impatient."

"It won't have a chance to be. We're already talking of a community project for setting out trees there next April. And then we'll tackle the campus and the streets of Amherst. I have great dreams, Emily."

"I'm glad you've found your railroad and politics so happily," she commented with a smile.

We both came home a little "newer" from our drive and our good long talk. And I couldn't help wondering why I let my life become so cluttered that I often let Emily get crowded out.

That fall of '58 two of the Newman cousins came to live at the Evergreens—Clara, fourteen, and Anna, twelve. Clara soon became a special friend of her cousin Emily next door, who took charge of her musical education and began teaching her chords on the piano at once.

With Clara and Anna on hand to run errands, the flow of communications between the two Dickinson houses was facilitated. Frequent notes went back and forth. Emily's famous rich, dark gingerbread would arrive, and Sue's cream puffs would go back on the plate. One of Emily's choice blossoms would grace our breakfast table; one of Vinnie's magazines would come marked for Sue to read; one of Sue's new books would go over for the girls. And occasionally Emily would send Sue a poem. I felt a nostalgic interest in one of them that came at this time, reminiscent of the fall Emily and I had chosen the white pines for the grove.

> The morns are meeker than they were—
> The nuts are getting brown—
> The berry's cheek is plumper—
> The Rose is out of town.
>
> The Maple wears a gayer scarf—
> The field a scarlet gown—
> Lest I sh'd be old-fashioned
> I'll put a trinket on.

"A bright leaf in her hair!" I exclaimed.

"No one in the world can say more about autumn in eight lines, Austin," Sue mused. "If Emily can write like this in her twenties, what will she be doing in her thirties?"

While Emily was capturing in a few words the essence of the peaceful Amherst countryside, she kept up an interest in political matters agitating the rest of the country. Out in Illinois a lanky lawyer of pioneer stock, a member of the new Republican party, was debating often and at length with a suave Democrat for a seat in the Senate. The Lincoln-Douglas debates were reported fully in Samuel Bowle's paper.

Father refused to take Abraham Lincoln seriously. "Just a local politician," he declared. "And I'm afraid all this ranting about 'A house divided' does more harm than good. Minor politicians like Lincoln will drop by the wayside, and the slavery issue will work itself out quietly."

I wondered if he was right. Actually, instead of working itself out quietly, the slavery issue became more and more pressing. In a melodramatic plot to liberate the slaves, a fanatical abolitionist, John Brown, captured the Federal arsenal at Harper's Ferry. He was soon taken by force and sentenced to death, and newspapers were full of the story. Emily grieved to read the accounts. She believed in the abolitionist cause, as she believed in all freedom, but she couldn't accept violence as a solution even though men like Emerson were calling John Brown a hero.

The books we younger Dickinsons exchanged that Christmas showed we were more concerned with literature than with current events. Vinnie gave Sue Dr. Holland's new book of poetry. Sue gave Emily *Adam Bede*, by George Eliot. And Emily gave Sue *Recollections of the Last Days of Shelley and Byron.*

As time went on, I felt that Emily's questing interest was centered on an ever-present eternity rather than on the passing moment. It wasn't that she considered the goings-on around her too trivial for attention. It just was that her eagerness for time to read and to think crowded out the time for personal contact. She seemed to be searching for something. Not that she confided in me. But I felt that she was groping for a deeper understanding of life than most of us bothered our heads about. A poem she sent Sue at this time showed how her mind was reaching out . . . toward horizons that were beyond me.

> Exultation is the going
> Of an inland soul to sea,
> Past the houses—past the headlands—
> Into deep Eternity—
>
> Bred as we, among the mountains,
> Can the sailor understand
> The divine intoxication
> Of the first league out from land?

We Dickinsons could hardly believe the happenings on the political scene in the spring of 1860. Seward failed to get the Republican nomination for the presidency, and Lincoln was nominated in his stead. "What has a splitter of rails to do with being President of the United States?" Father sputtered. We were even more amazed in November when Lincoln was actually elected President.

Dissension between the North and South was gnawing at the already frayed ties of union. Before Mr. Lincoln was even inaugurated, seven southern states seceded from the Union. What would the new President do? We all wondered about it. War between North and South was unthinkable. Yet for the North to give in on the slavery issue was unthinkable, too. When newspaper accounts became too much for Emily, she would escape to the peace of her garden.

While big events were shaping themselves on the national scene, life went on quietly in Amherst. Mother, recovered at last from her long illness, was up and around again, entering into the social life of the village and supervising the household. Her greatest worry was the poor health of her favorite sister, our Aunt Lavinia Norcross. Early in the winter Vinnie left for Boston to help our young cousins, Fanny and Loo, take care of her.

Without Vin to shepherd her, Emily was like a lost lamb. She carried on resolutely enough, but without Vinnie's efficiency. I could imagine her kneading Father's favorite rye-and-Indian-corn bread one moment and jotting down lines of poetry on a scrap of brown paper the next, while the soup boiled over on the stove.

Soon after Vinnie went to Boston, Emily had an unexpected caller. At the time it seemed an event of no more than passing importance. But as the years went by, Sue and I realized it was something more than passing. How much more we never knew because we respected the sacred domain of Emily's privacy.

I found out about Emily's caller inadvertently one breezy March evening when I told Sue I was going to run over to the homestead to hear the latest news about Aunt Lavinia.

"See if you can find out who came in the carriage today," Sue called out as I started for the door. "A man got out and went to the door."

"Probably one of the Norcross or Dickinson relatives," I said.

"With Vinnie in Boston, and your mother out making calls, that left Emily home alone," Sue objected. "Can you imagine Emily being enough interested in any caller to keep him all of an hour?"

"Maybe it was Willie Dickinson."

"No, it was an older man. I never saw him before."

I laughed. "With trees in the way and a March wind blowing, how could you hope to recognize anyone several hundred feet away, Sue? Well, we'll see."

I expected to find Emily in the kitchen, drying dishes for Margaret, as was her custom. But Margaret was drying her own dishes.

"Where's Emily?" I asked.

"Nowhere but in her room, silent as the winter snow, Mr. Austin." Fat and good-natured, a year older than Emily, Margaret talked with an Irish lilt that made her a perfect target for Vinnie's mimicry.

"Ill?"

"She was fit as a cricket before that man called this afternoon," Margaret sputtered. "She's been a-mooning with herself ever since. Even your Father couldn't budge her down for supper. And the tray I fetched her is still a-setting there before her door, I wouldn't doubt."

Margaret told me how a gentleman got out of a carriage and knocked and asked for Miss Emily Dickinson. "I looked him up and down without letting on, and I'd say he was medium build, and he had dark eyes a-shining through his glasses. And a deep voice the like of which I've never heard in Amherst. 'Will you kindly tell Miss Dickinson that Dr. Wordsworth is calling?' he asks."

Quickly I searched my mind. We knew no one by the name of Wordsworth, aside from the English poet. Might it have been . . . "Might the name have been Wadsworth, Margaret?"

She thought a moment. "I'm not saying it couldn't."

Emily never mentioned Dr. Wadsworth's visit to Sue or me. She talked to Vinnie about it later, but Vinnie was too loyal to breathe a word. I never knew what Emily and her clergyman talked about that afternoon. Poetry? Life? Immortality? I only knew that it spurred Emily on to spending more time with her thoughts and her writing. For months after that visit the lamp in her room burned longer into the night.

Sue's curiosity kept nudging her. She and Emily were close, yet fiercely independent at the same time. And no one was a more ardent champion of Emily's talents than Sue, who took delight in comparing Emily with well-known writers.

"Maybe Emily doesn't entirely agree with Emerson on transcendentalism," Sue said on one of those rare evenings when we were home alone, reading, "but she certainly has two things in common with him." I looked up from my book as Sue went on, "They both have an intense love of nature and a high-spirited joy in living.

Why, sometimes Emerson almost sounds drunk with it. Listen to this from *Bacchus*: 'Bring me wine, but wine which never grew in the belly of the grape.' And there's something quite similar in his *Essays*."

Putting down my book, I listened to Sue read in her rich, full voice: " 'The poet's habit of living should be set on a key so low that the common influences should delight him. His cheerfulness should be the gift of the sunlight; the air should suffice for his inspiration; and he should be tipsy with water.' "

I smiled. "Then Emily must be a poet of the first magnitude, Sue."

Emily, probably at Sue's suggestion, wrote a poem as her comment on the wine and tipsiness of the poet, and Sue found that it improved on Emerson in practically every line. "Instead of being merely cheerful with sunlight," she told me, "Emily is *inebriate of air*. And instead of being tipsy with water, she's a *debauche of dew*. I'm continually amazed at the way she handles words, Austin. I tried to get her to send the poem, anonymously of course, to the *Republican* for its Original Poetry column."

"Samuel Bowles would have to pass on it, and poetry isn't his weakness. Anyway, she'll never send it."

After months of wavering, Emily finally did find courage to send in the poem, and it was published almost immediately. But her pleasure at seeing it in print was marred by the changes made in three of the lines.

Sue sighed. "She's such a perfectionist . . . in her choice of words, her choice of thoughts. Now I suppose

131

she'll never submit another thing. If only fame meant more to her, she'd be willing to put up with editorial changes. But the desire for fame was left out of her make-up. I wonder if I can recall the way she put it one time." Sue thought a moment, her eyes on the fire in the grate, then tentatively quoted:

A little bread, a crust—a crumb,
A little trust, a Demijohn,
Can keep the soul alive . . .

Just the other day, Austin, she said that if she could make us proud of her sometime, a long way off, she would ask nothing more."

"That's just it, Sue. Emily doesn't care for fame in a worldly sense; she just wants response from those she loves. She gets it from you, and that's why she shows more of her poems to you than to anyone else."

"But she should try for wider circulation. I would . . . if I could write like that."

"But you're not Emily," I answered.

Aunt Lavinia's death in April struck me a hard blow, even though I had been expecting it. She had been uncommonly good to me those first weeks when I was teaching at Endicott. "It's the old problem of death again," I said to Emily as we sat together in the homestead kitchen after the evening work was over. "What can we count on?"

"I keep wondering if Aunt Lavinia sees us now," Emily mused. "Strange, the only one we can't find out about in his native town is Death. But I feel sure he can't put an end to the beyond. Take some of my surety, Austin."

I, one of the pillars of the First Parish Church, turned to Emily, the impenitent, to find consolation.

CHAPTER 10

MEANWHILE the war which we did not believe could happen was drawing closer.

Lincoln was inaugurated in March of '61. Five weeks later Confederate soldiers fired on Fort Sumter. Lincoln immediately sent out a call for 75,000 men, and the war was on.

I was surprised at the way the young men of Amherst answered the call. Professor Tyler preached a sermon in the college chapel on heroism and self-sacrifice and when the service was over, a hundred students volunteered, a goodly proportion of the student body. The next day Father addressed the crowd at a flag-raising ceremony. People gathered in the streets. Young Frazar Stearns, son of the president of the College, enlisted and left for the front. When I wished him luck, he said, "I hope, Mr. Dickinson, I can do something that will make Amherst proud of me, in a small way."

I liked Frazar. I'd known him since he was a youngster and had watched him grow up to be like his father —alert, kindly, and courteous. I hated to think of his going away to fight.

Emily was amazed that Frazar was old enough to go. "Where have I been while he was growing up?" she wanted to know. "Oh, Austin, I dread to think of all the young men going to war before they have had a chance to live."

I had no desire whatever to enlist. I was thirty-two, involved in a full and busy life. The last thing I wanted to do was to leave home, except for occasional trips to New York to add to my art collection. Besides, after almost five years of marriage, Sue and I were expecting our first child, and we Dickinsons were all excited at the prospect. War seemed very far away, even with the College emptying and the town loud with excitement. Surely it would be a short war. How could the South hold out against the superior numbers and wealth of the North?

Our son was born on the 19th of June. Emily sent a message that she wouldn't come over right away for fear of joggling one so small he could fit in a cup. Father beamed and offered his congratulations. "We shall have to enlarge the office, Austin, now that we are Dickinson, Dickinson, and Dickinson." He was as pleased as I was

135

that the Dickinson name would be carried on to another generation. I went about exulting, but trying not to show it.

For months Sue and I couldn't decide on a name for our son. Vinnie suggested that in the meantime we call him Jack, short for Union Jack, so he'd at least know which side he was on. And so Jack he became until we named him after his grandfather. Father, of course, was delighted. Little Edward Dickinson became "Ned" to all of us, and a special joy to his Aunt Emily next door.

And Emily needed joy that fall. She seemed to be withdrawing more and more into herself, as if something she could not speak about was sealing her away from us. I said nothing about it except to Vin, thinking that perhaps Emily was suffering from ill health.

Vin shrugged when I questioned her. "What makes you think there's anything wrong?" she asked. Loyalty was always one of her strong points.

But by the latter part of October even Vin was showing concern. A visit from Samuel Bowles brought matters to a head.

Samuel Bowles was a favorite guest at both houses, and between visits we all kept in touch with him through letters. Originally a friend of Father's through their mutual interest in the College, Bowles had become one of my best friends. He was only three years my senior. Whenever he came to Amherst, he stayed with Sue and me, and many were the joint supper parties we had with the Dickinsons from the other house.

Emily and Sue were special friends of Bowles. They

matched wits with him, each in her own way. He was continually reminding me of my good fortune in having both a wife and a sister with first-rate minds.

Bowles had been in ill health for some time. He wrote me in mid-October that he hoped to be well enough to drive to Northampton for one of the water cures. The cure helped and, before going back to Springfield, he came over to Amherst for a visit. I looked forward to it with more than usual anticipation, not only because I was eager to see him, but also because I thought his visit would be good for Emily.

What was my consternation when Emily failed to put in an appearance!

After Bowles left, I stormed over to the mansion determined to have it out with her. Vin was alone in the kitchen, putting things on a tray. "Where's Emily?" I demanded. "She can't treat Sam Bowles this way. It's one thing to stay home from a party, but she can't do this to Sam Bowles."

"Don't be cross, Austin."

"As I remember, you didn't approve yourself. I heard you trying to make excuses to Mr. Sam, and I could sense your impatience behind it all."

She turned to face me, and even in the dimness of lamplight I couldn't help seeing her blink her eyes to keep back the tears. "I hope Mr. Bowles didn't sense my impatience. Yes, I did blame Emily. I even went and told her what I thought when she said she didn't want any supper tonight. But, oh, Austin . . ."

We heard the door open into the kitchen from the

"Northwest Passage," and there stood Emily, pale and calm. "I thought I heard your voice, Austin. I've been trying to fortify myself." She saw the half-filled tray on the table. "Oh, thank you, Vinnie. But not now, not until Austin and I are friends again." She looked up at me. "We'd best go to the quiet of my room, don't you think?"

She led the way up to her room, and we sat there in front of the Franklin stove, where a small October fire glowed. Near the window a candle burned on her work-table. It was full of papers and her open lexicon, as if she had left a sentence unfinished when she heard my voice.

"Emily," I began, "Mr. Sam was looking forward to seeing you, talking to you, bantering with you. I'm sure it was one of the reasons he came so soon after his illness. You can't do this to him. You're going to have to apologize."

"I'll apologize," she said meekly. "I'll write him tomorrow. But don't be cross with me, Austin. Please don't scold. He needed the light side of me, after his illness, and I wasn't able to give it. I'm not feeling light these days. Just lonely . . . awfully lonely."

"And yet you give up a chance to see Sam Bowles? What kind of loneliness is this? It doesn't make sense, Emily."

Her voice was quiet as she answered, her words measured. "It's another kind of loneliness that has nothing to do with friends. And I suffer from it. Believe me, I do."

138

I could see by her face that she spoke the truth, yet I was at a loss to understand. "But why . . . if loneliness oppresses you, do you choose to be alone so much?"

With a despairing gesture she answered, "Being with people makes you and Vinnie and Sue and Father feel more alive. But it doesn't do that for me, only for a very small part of me. Most of me feels smothered by the talking and bantering."

She was no longer looking at me but staring at the sudden flicker of light as some bark caught fire. "I feel the need for immensity . . . and when I touch it, all is well . . . but it happens so seldom. Between times I'm terribly alone." She was having a hard time finding words to express what she meant. "Yet in a way I'm rich, richer than I can tell, because I *do* occasionally feel at one with something big. Then I'm lonely again . . . and in my writing, too. Trying to put thoughts and feelings into words is a lonely occupation, Austin."

"I can see that it would be."

"Yet I am driven to it, driven by a force that makes me cold and hot by turns." She paused and then went on in a voice so low I could scarcely hear. "And there's something else . . . something I can't talk about that takes the heart out of me."

We both were silent. The clock ticked. The fire burned low. Finally Emily went on. "I don't ask you to understand me. I don't understand myself. I only ask you to have compassion on me, Austin. That's what I need . . . your compassion."

How well she knew me! What could I do? What

could I say but promise to remember not to upbraid her again? Repentent of the spirit in which I had come, I rose to go.

That year 1862 was a year of turmoil—not only for Emily, but for the North and South. The war went on blunderingly, we all thought. Lincoln had trouble finding leaders who would push the army into advancing toward the enemy. For the first time we were able to keep abreast of current events by telegraph, Father having been instrumental in getting the telegraph lines extended to Amherst. News of a few minor victories, too few and too minor, trickled in over the wires.

Then in mid-March news came of a northern victory at strongly-fortified New Bern in North Carolina, where Frazar Stearns was serving as an adjutant. Federal troops captured the town. Amherst heard the report with pride and excitement. I was away from the office for several hours that afternoon. When I returned, Father came and stood by my desk.

"Frazar is killed," he said. "At New Bern."

I was completely stunned. "Frazar!" Only a short while before he had wished he could do something to make Amherst proud of him—in a small way. For me the glory went out of the victory at New Bern. Hardly knowing what I was doing, I reached for my broad-brimmed hat and hurried up Main Street. "Frazar is killed, Frazar is killed," kept drumming in my head. Instead of turning in at the Evergreens, I went on to the homestead. I had to see Emily. Even in her turmoil, part of her seemed always to be at peace. I hoped to find consolation in talking to her, and I was not disappointed.

We talked for a long time, and I came away with the perspective I needed. Never once did Emily mention the troubles she kept locked in her heart.

I knew that Sue had been aware for some time that Emily was suffering emotionally. More than once she remarked that Emily acted as if she were hopelessly in love—but hopelessly in love with whom? Emmons and other young men Emily had known and liked had long since moved away. The only man Sue could think of was Emily's Philadelphia clergyman, Dr. Wadsworth. "For months after his visit she seemed to be living on a different planet," Sue commented. "But why the turmoil since last fall?"

Then in mid-March Sue brought me a copy of the *Republican* and pointed out an announcement about Dr. Wadsworth. He had accepted a call to a big church in San Francisco. "Do you think he told Emily ahead of time?" she asked. "As long ago as last fall? Do you think it has been part of her trouble—that Dr. Wadsworth is moving so far away?"

I remembered Emily saying there was something she couldn't talk about. But that it was Dr. Wadsworth seemed to me too rash a speculation. I handed back the paper. "Perhaps he and Emily do share a stimulating exchange of letters, a love for poetry, a search for truth," I said. "But Dr. Wadsworth is a married man of great dignity and standing. I can't think she has fallen in love with him . . . unless she builds castles out of dreams."

"But who else can it be?" Sue persisted. "Or is she just in love with love?"

As if to add fuel to the fire of Sue's conjecture, Margaret brought over a poem buried in the curled petals of a hyacinth long before our hyacinths were in bloom. Sue gave me the slip of paper to read after supper. "Would you include this among the guessing games?" she asked.

I read it carefully. It began with an arresting simile: "He fumbles at your Soul as Players at the Keys," and built up to a tremendous climax where he "deals one imperial Thunderbolt that scalps your naked soul."

"It's about a preacher obviously," I said, looking up. "One of the rare ones who stirs her to the depths. A revivalist?"

"I don't think so."

"Who, then?"

"Dr. Wadsworth, Austin. You've read more than once what an impression he makes, how people stand in line to hear him preach. I don't see how Emily can mean anyone else. And it goes right in with . . . well, with Emily's emotional upset."

"She's certainly in a turmoil about something," I conceded. "And I suppose one guess is as good as another."

A poem written in this troubled period came to light many years later. It tells better than any words of mine the depth of Emily's misery. Had Sue been right, after all?

I got so I could hear his name
Without—Tremendous gain—
That Stop-sensation—on my Soul—
And Thunder—in the Room—

I got so I could walk across
That Angle in the floor,
Where he turned so, and I turned—how—
And all our Sinew tore—

I got so I could stir the Box—
In which his letters grew
Without that forcing, in my breath—
As Staples—driven through—

Of course, Father—always sensitive to Emily's moods
—noticed her tenseness and abstractedness and worried
about her. "I wonder what has happened to Emily," he
said to me when she failed to come down to meet some
of his important friends. "She seems to care less and
less about the things that normally interest a young
woman: the sugaring-off parties, the picnics, the sleigh
rides. Have you any idea what's wrong, Austin?"

"Sue and I have been baffled, too," I answered and
left it at that. There was no use bringing up the name
of Dr. Wadsworth.

We were all concerned about Bowles's failing health
that year. Some obscure ailment made walking difficult,
and the burden of work on the *Republican* finally

proved too much for him. In desperation he left for Europe for a complete change and rest. He was away for seven months, and we all missed him, probably Emily more than any of us. They kept up a spirited correspondence, and I am sure she wrote him time and again how much she missed him, how deeply she yearned to see him.

A few weeks after Bowles's return from Europe he made a trip to Amherst to visit us, staying at our house as usual. Among other things, he was looking forward to a good talk with Emily. But again she failed him. She sent over a brief note saying that she could not see him.

"That you return to us alive, is better than a Summer," she wrote, showing that it was not lack of affection that kept her away.

I came into the library in time to hear Sue and Sam discussing the note and Emily. I paused in the doorway to listen, counting on Sue to take Emily's part, but ready to add words of my own if the need arose.

"The rascal!" Bowles chided, half in fun. Then, more seriously, "But I think she makes a mistake, even if she finds her lexicon more rewarding than much of the conversation in Amherst. Why can't she think her thoughts and still act like other women?"

"Why *should* Emily act like other women when she isn't like them?" Sue demanded. "Why does everyone think she should conform?"

"Because, my dear Sue, that's the natural way a person develops, a product of his times and his surroundings."

"But Emily is different. You know that as well as I do. And it takes time, *time*, to write the way Emily does, with such conciseness and penetration. It's not like dashing off copy for your newspaper, Mr. Sam." She caught sight of me in the doorway and beckoned to me with a lift of her head. "Come, Austin, explain how some of our greatest men have *not* been products of their times but have stood out against them. I must see how dinner is progressing." She gave Bowles one of her disarming smiles and left.

"I know what you're going to say, Austin," Bowles said quickly. "Emily has a right to live her own life. Well, I believe that, too. It's only that, selfishly, I'd like to have her more available, to explain some of her riddles, for one thing."

"You mean in her writing?"

Bowles nodded. "She sends me poems from time to time, with her letters or as part of them. I can't always figure out what she means."

"You're not the only one. It's a game she plays. She likes to keep us all guessing."

"Not long ago she sent me a strange bridal poem, something about being a wife without the sign. I'm completely baffled. It began . . . 'Title divine . . .'" He caught himself up short. "Wait! I wasn't suppose to tell. She said I must keep it to myself, on my honor. So forget it, Austin. You probably wouldn't know what it's about, anyway, any more than I do."

But I wasn't left entirely in the dark. A poem Emily sent over some time later struck me as being the one

Bowles had heedlessly talked about. In it Emily referred to herself as wife, born, bridaled, shrouded in a day. Sue and I puzzled over it. Even though we knew that Emily liked to be extravagant with words, we caught few glimmers of meaning. "The wife—without the Sign!" Whose wife?

Then one day Sue had an inspiration. "I don't believe it's an earthly poem at all, Austin. It's . . . well, mystical, you might say. I don't believe she's speaking of a mortal marriage, but of a union of the soul with the Lord. Remember the place in Revelation that speaks of the marriage of the soul—the place where the seven angels say: 'Come hither, I will shew thee the bride, the Lamb's wife.' "

"Mystical? You may be right."

"You know how much Emily likes Henry Vaughan's poetry," Sue went on. "He speaks of seeing eternity as a great ring of light which the heavenly Bridegroom provided for his bride."

"It all sounds pretty vague to me." I sighed. "I wonder if we'll ever know what she means."

Emily never came now to the social evenings Sue and I gave at our house. They were the talk of the town because of Sue's brilliance as a hostess. It rather amused me that Sue could quite understand Emily's refusal to attend other social affairs, yet be somewhat vexed with her for not wanting to come to ours. I pointed out to Sue that her wit could be ruthless at times and that it probably upset Emily.

Sue tossed her head. "I suppose you're right. She'd

have me spoil a good story about someone, or at least make me self-conscious in the telling. And I simply have to have a fresh stock of gossip to keep the conversation from lagging." Then she added wistfully, "I miss her though."

One evening when I came home from the office, Sue brought me a scrap of paper. "What do you make of this?" she asked. "Emily sent it over this morning in answer to my urging that she come to our party tonight."

I read the poem aloud, slowly. Emily's handwriting was harder than ever to decipher these days, and her punctuation more baffling.

> The Soul that hath a Guest
> Doth seldom go abroad—
> Diviner Crowd at Home—
> Obliterate the need—
>
> And Courtesy forbid
> A Host's departure when
> Upon Himself be visiting
> The Emperor of Men—

What did she mean about having a guest? Not her clergymen. He was safely settled way off in San Francisco. I handed the paper back. "What's your guess, Sue?"

"I think she's talking like some of the English religious writers she reads. It may sound queer for me to say this, Austin, but I believe she means the Lord is visiting her—the Emperor of Men."

I had to admit the possibility.

"Emily is much closer to the Lord than we are," Sue said thoughtfully, "for all our interest in the Church. It may be that His presence is so real that He seems to be visiting her. And perhaps that is her salvation at this point."

"I sincerely hope her love for the Emperor of Men is bringing her a comfort that love for a man is denying her," I replied. "Heaven knows she needs comfort from somewhere."

In her turmoil Emily was burning the midnight oil at a great rate. Through the trees we could see the west windows of her room on the second floor of the mansion. No matter what time of night I happened to look over there, even long after midnight, I would see a light burning and would recall her words about what lonely work writing was. But I had no idea until many years later what tremendous creative power must have been driving her on, so great was her output of poems in 1862, the year of her deepest stress.

And yet in spite of the turmoil within her, Emily retained her sympathetic interest in those around her. It often seemed to me that she had the ability to live on two levels at the same time—the level of the mind and spirit, and the level of everyday activities. She was ever-a solicitous friend of the stableboy and yardman, sending little gifts for an anniversary or an illness in the family. And they in turn staunchly defended her against town gossip. She was untiring in the attentions she paid to neighbors in trouble, and thoughtful of those closest to her, too.

I remember how quietly helpful she was to Clara Newman at this time. Cousin Clara was worried for fear she would fail her difficult high school examinations. She often carried her worries to the other house, to Emily, and I noticed that she always came back with new confidence.

Before Clara hurried off to her ordeal on examination day, a note arrived from next door. Clara's face flushed with pleasure as she read it to us. "A little flower is sitting beside me waiting to be a Crown."

Clara was late getting home. She hadn't time to stop and tell Emily she was confident she had passed. We were just sitting down to supper when the maid came in from the kitchen to tell Clara she was wanted at the door. She ran out, returning a few minutes later with a flower. She showed it to us proudly and said with a tremor in her voice, "Cousin Emily stood there in the dusk, holding out the flower. She said it was so impatient to be a crown, it insisted on bringing her over."

How like Emily, coming down from her heights to crown a wayfarer.

That was the year Emily and Sue could hardly wait for the April issue of the *Atlantic Monthly* to arrive. It had been announced that there was to be an article by Thomas Wentworth Higginson, entitled "Letter to a Young Contributor." All would-be writers were urged to read it as a test of their latent power.

Emily was interested, of course, because of her writing; Sue because of her interest in Emily's writing and in Thomas Wentworth Higginson himself. She admired the man for his championship of Anthony Burns, the fugitive slave, years before; and for taking a stand for liberal causes, like women's rights. She had even tried to get a photograph of him through Samuel Bowles.

Higginson's article quite lived up to Emily's expectations. He thought that language could become so saturated with warm life that every sentence would palpitate. "There may be years of crowded passion in a word, and half a life in a sentence." That was the kind of writing Emily was trying to achieve.

"I wonder if my words palpitate," she mused.

"Why don't you write Higginson and find out?" I suggested.

She looked at me quickly. "I'll do it, Austin! I'll ask him if my verse is alive, if it breathes."

I urged her to write immediately, before she changed her mind. "And enclose four or five of your poems, Emily."

One of the poems she enclosed I had special reason to remember. Only the month before, Samuel Bowles had printed it anonymously in the *Republican*, and it was one of the few of Emily's poems published during her lifetime. "Safe in their alabaster chambers" didn't happen to be one of my favorites, because death was a gruesome subject to me. But Sue rated the poem very high, even though she felt that the second stanza didn't go with the ghostly cold of the first stanza which, she said, always made her turn to the fire to warm herself.

As for me, I preferred to have poetry warm me by itself without making me turn to the fire. And one of

Emily's winter poems, written about this time, did just that. The whole canvas of a snowstorm unfolded before me as I read:

> It sifts from Leaden Sieves—
> It powders all the Wood.
> It fills with Alabaster Wool
> The Wrinkles of the Road—
>
> It makes an Even Face
> Of Mountain, and of Plain—
> Unbroken Forehead from the East
> Unto the East again—

I never did get to know what Higginson thought of Emily's poetry. Putting two and two together, though, Sue and I came to the conclusion that he must have said something about her verses not yet being ready for publication. Evidently for him, outstanding literary critic though he was, poetry had to be in the conventional mold, perfectly rhymed and unbroken in beat. Emily broke all traditions, making her rhyme scheme and meter suit her mood at the time. Still, Higginson must have sent words of praise and given her encouragement, for year after year she continued to write him occasional letters, enclosing poems for his reaction.

After Emily's distress was over, she sent Sue a poem that seemed to leave little doubt that the bridal poem had referred to the marriage of the Soul.

Given in Marriage unto Thee
Oh thou Celestial Host—
Bride of the Father and the Son,
Bride of the Holy Ghost.

This poem gave Sue an opening to bring up the subject with Emily. What she found out amazed her. Emily confessed that she had had a strange experience during the year of her greatest stress, an experience so transforming that she wouldn't trade it for all the rest of life.

"What kind of experience?" I demanded.

"Emily tried to tell me, but it was difficult. Evidently it came like a flash of lightning that struck no one but herself . . . a 'waylaying light,' like the light that blinded Saint Paul on the road to Damascus."

"I've often wondered about that blinding light of Paul's. Do you think it was real, Sue?"

"There's no doubt in Emily's mind that it was real. And in some strange way she says she found the explanation of life in that sudden flash." Sue spoke almost with awe.

I tried to imagine the impact of such an experience. "Did it happen only once?"

"Only once in full force, as near as I could gather. In her year of quick calamity, as she called it. She's had small flashes, too, before and since. It was after one of these that she wrote the poem we puzzled over so much, the one that begins, 'Just lost when I was saved! Just felt the world go by!' "

"Yes, I remember."

"She couldn't give me more than an inkling of what happened, Austin. And even with all her wizardy with words, she can't put much of it down on paper. But it seems to have helped her get over her turmoil."

CHAPTER 11

FATHER turned sixty on New Year's Day of 1863. He carried his years well. Tall, dignified, vital, he kept up a busy law practice and insurance business and invested in real estate as a sideline. Yet he always found time for church, community, and College affairs. We Dickinsons were proud of the honors that kept coming to him as one of the leading citizens of Amherst.

Like the rest of us, he worried over the war and hoped it would soon end, though not until the rebellion was crushed between the upper and nether millstone, as he expressed it. He seemed surprised that a man like Thomas Wentworth Higginson was willing to drop his profession to go to war. Higginson had accepted command of a Negro regiment in South Carolina, the first Negro regiment in the Union army. To Sue he was more of a hero than ever, and she frankly told Father how much she admired Higginson for getting into the fight. Father maintained a stony silence. Far from wanting me to enlist, he was worrying for fear I would soon be drafted.

Some inscrutable poems came across the yard to Sue at this time. For the most part I was content to leave the unraveling to her. But whenever one of Emily's nature poems came our way, I felt she was speaking words I could understand. She wrote about sunset dropping a purple raveling in the pond, and about November hanging his granite hat upon a nail of plush, and about wind kneading the grass and throwing away the road. But even with nature she could be baffling.

"Why the quotation marks?" I asked Sue one day when she showed me a poem with nature in quotation marks.

"Don't you think it's because she feels there's more to it than just what we see and hear?" I must have looked blank for Sue added, "It's the squirrel, the eclipse, and the bumblebee, as she says here, but something more, too."

I reread the last four lines for further light:

> Nature is what we know—
> Yet have no art to say—
> So impotent Our Wisdom is
> To her Simplicity.

155

Then Sue recalled that Emily had said that nature was heaven, too, and that was why she had not the art to put it into words.

I shrugged. "Her poems don't have to be philosophical to suit me."

Sue spoke up quickly, her dark eyes afire. "My favorites are the ones with a vein of philosophy running through them. They're the ones that will live, Austin. Long after Emily is gone."

Did she really mean that, or was it just her habit of wanting to say something startling? I looked at her sharply. Yes, she meant it; conviction was written all over her face.

Another poem of Emily's appeared in print about this time, in a small new magazine published in New York by a cousin of ours. How he got a copy of the poem I had no idea. Certainly Emily never gave it to him with the idea of publication. It undoubtedly caused more than a few raised eyebrows for its light treatment of the Sabbath. Emily rarely went to church any more, but until this poem appeared, the good citizens of Amherst didn't know how she felt about it. I wondered how many of them would see the little magazine and hoped for her sake they would be few. As for me, I couldn't help thinking how characteristic the poem was of Emily in its brightness and candor and independence . . . with a touch of mischief.

Some keep the Sabbath going to Church—
I keep it, staying at Home—
With a Bobolink for a Chorister—
And an Orchard, for a Dome—

Some keep the Sabbath in Surplice—
I just wear my Wings—
And instead of tolling the Bell, for Church,
Our little Sexton—sings.

God preaches, a noted Clergyman—
And the sermon is never long,
So instead of going to Heaven, at last—
I'm going, all along.

Within a few weeks another of Emily's poems was published in the *Republican*. According to Sue, who treasured all the clippings, this was the fifth poem to be published. It was about the sun leaping across the sky like a leopard, blazing in gold at sunrise, and quenching in purple when it laid its spotted face on the horizon to die. It was one of my favorites.

As Emily's emotional turmoil subsided, she began to experience a new suffering. Her much-abused eyes began to rebel. Father was the first to notice it. He came upon her sitting among her beloved plants in the conservatory with a dark scarf around her eyes. It was just to rest her eyes from the light she told him, but it troubled him.

When he questioned me about it, I agreed that she

was probably using her eyes too much at night. "I often see her light burning late at night, Father. She's driving herself toward something . . . I don't know what. You remember how my eyes went back on me when I was teaching in Boston and reading too long by lamplight and candlelight."

"I must put a stop to the late hours!" Father exclaimed. "Emily's eyes are more important than anything she might be using them for."

Although neither Sue nor I had noticed anything wrong with Emily's eyes until then, we both had noticed a subtle change in her after her period of greatest stress. We couldn't put a finger on it. Like Shakespeare, she seemed to be viewing the world as a stage. Once she likened it to a drum pursued of little boys. I couldn't go along with her there except for the dreary hours I had to spend at the office. But my plan for beautifying Amherst, my art collection, and my dream of building a new church seemed more important than a drum pursued of little boys.

By the next spring Emily's eyes were so bad that there was no hiding her distress. One day I found her in tears with an open book on her lap.

"Oh, Austin, the print blurs so I can't see it at all. Am I going blind? How could I live without my books and my writing? How could I bear it?"

I did what I could to reassure her, and that very day Father decided that Vinnie should take her to Boston to start her on a series of treatments with an eye specialist. The thought of leaving home for an indefinite period appalled her. Carlo would feel that she had deserted him, and he needed the assurance of being loved now that he was getting old. And what would become of her plants? And when Vinnie left her in Boston, how would she get on alone? Emily's only consolation was that she could stay at the boardinghouse where our Norcross cousins, Loo and Fanny, had been living since the death of their father.

With Emily gone, the house next door seemed dark and woebegone. I was depressed to think of her off there in Boston with bandaged eyes, yearning to look at spring, yet trying to be patient. But when Ned's third birthday arrived, it was evident that no bandages covered the eyes of her mind. She couldn't resist writing Ned a few lines: "Emily knows a Man who drives a Coach like a Thimble, and turns the Wheel all day with his Heel— His name is Bumblebee." Ned crowed over the poem just as Emily knew he would.

Sue had a nostalgic letter from Emily in September. She was worried about some of her plants. Abby Wood Bliss had sent seeds from Syria, where she and her husband were in charge of a mission school, and Emily was especially concerned about these foreign plants she had raised. And she was full of homesick questions. "Are the Apples ripe? Have the Wild Geese crossed? Did you save the seed to the pond Lily?"

I could well imagine how Emily suffered from being "in prison" for months on end, a hundred miles from the place she loved most. Yet I knew perfectly well that she had her moments of exaltation. Her mind would be free. She would be jotting down words and phrases, entertaining unseen guests I knew nothing of.

It was late November before she came home. I felt like celebrating Thanksgiving all over again and rushed to the homestead full of anticipation. But I saw at once that Emily was far from well. Carlo seemed to tower over her. "He won't leave me," she said with a whimsical smile. "He yowled when he saw me, as if I were a ghost. Have I changed so much?"

I assured her that she looked pretty good to me. "And how about the eyes?" I asked hopefully.

"Sometimes easy, Austin, sometimes sad. The light offends them. Vinnie can't see why I don't get well, and I can't, either. Can you?" She grasped my hand. "And now tell me all about you and Sue and Ned and Clara and Anna. Oh, I was so afraid you might be like Mr. Higginson and run off to war. And what would we do without you?"

"I was drafted and had to pay five hundred dollars for a substitute," I told her. "But Father didn't think any price too high."

"Nor do I!" she exclaimed.

Emily's eyes were really little better than when she went away. Father worried. When winter was over, he had Vinnie take her to Boston again for another series of treatments.

A week or two before they left, Sue was prostrated with grief over the sudden death of her sister, Harriet Cutler. The three sisters—Harriet, Mattie, and Sue—had always been unusually close, and the unexpected breaking of the tie hit Sue hard. We had been drifting somewhat apart, I felt. Her gayness, her desire to shine at social gatherings, her cutting wit often left me thinking that Emily was right about the world being a drum. But in her grief Sue turned to me, and we felt a depth of understanding and sympathy that had been eluding us for some time.

That was the spring the war ended. At last! I could picture Loo and Fanny reading the news to Emily—about Lee surrendering to Grant on Palm Sunday at Appomattox Courthouse in Virginia. And then came that shocking night of Good Friday when Lincoln was shot at the theater. The whole country was stunned. I knew Emily's grief would be intense.

It was a sorrowful April, with Emily away and Sue still unable to pull herself together, and Ned ill again. Because he had never been strong, the recurrent attacks of fever that afflicted him kept us full of concern.

Now on top of everything else I had a sad clipping to send Emily. Helen Fiske Hunt, who had already lost her husband in an accident, now lost her son of diphtheria. Her other son had died some years before. Life had been hard on Helen since those tomboy days in Amherst. Everyone bears some sort of cross, I thought, as I sealed my letter to Emily.

In mid-June Sue had a few lines of verse from Emily, enough to assure us that although her eyes were bandaged and her activities limited, her mind was still ranging unfettered.

When Emily finally came home in October, a minor

catastrophe had struck the homestead. Mighty, good-natured, dependable Margaret had left to be married, and Father was in the throes of trying to find someone to take her place. Emily had to plunge into housework. But this time her eyes were really better, and some of her strength had returned.

"I'll never go away again," she told me emphatically. And she never did.

Sue and Emily were overjoyed to be living next door again after all the months of separation. In spite of their occasional misunderstandings and temporary rifts, they depended on each other. Sue was flattered that Emily turned to her more than to anyone else for response to the poems. She had championed Emily's poetry from the beginning. Emily on her side relied on Sue's approbation. Their relationship, I often thought, was unique for sisters-in-law.

But Sue was quick-tempered and high-handed and liked to have her own way. This often bothered me, and I knew it would bother Emily if the highhandedness ever involved her poetry. A few months after Emily's return from Boston the inevitable happened.

Our good friend, Samuel Bowles, had been asking for more of Emily's poetry for the *Republican*, but Emily demurred. Then early in February, Bowles came to Amherst for a few days and stayed with us. Sue showed him a late poem of Emily's, a poem about a snake, "a narrow fellow in the grass." He exclaimed in admiration as he read some of it aloud:

The Grass divides as with a Comb—
A spotted shaft is seen—
And then it closes at your feet
And opens further on—

He likes a Boggy Acre
A Floor too cool for Corn—

Bowles looked up in amazement. "How did that girl ever know that a boggy field isn't good for corn? I'd like to have this for the paper."

Sue hesitated only a fraction of a second. "All right, you may have it, if you publish it anonymously."

Bowles ran the poem on the front page of the *Republican* on Valentine's Day, 1866. Emily was indignant, indignant that Sue hadn't asked her consent. "She robbed me of it, Austin," she accused. "Robbed me of it."

I tried to console her. "Hardly that, Emily. Her name isn't on it."

"But it was between Sue and me. And, look, they changed the punctuation in one line, so it spoils the meaning."

"You don't have to send her any more poems, if you want to punish her."

Emily shook her head mournfully. "But Sue understands them better than anyone else."

It was true, of course. And before long the rift was covered over . . . but never completely forgotten.

After the episode of "a narrow fellow in the grass" fewer poems came across the lawn to Sue. Gingerbread came, choice flowers, unexpected tidbits, brief notes, but fewer poems. Was Emily still too deeply hurt to want to share her thoughts with Sue, or had her creative flame burned down to a sedate glow?

Perhaps Carlo's death had something to do with Emily's flagging inspiration. She grieved for him. For fifteen years he had been her constant companion; she never even went into the garden without him. When I came to offer my sympathy, she said she would never get another dog.

"Only one sun. One moon. One Carlo," she murmured. "Vinnie's cats are many and changing. But only one Carlo."

Emily seemed to be pushing herself to get through the daily round of duties. I noticed that her light went out earlier, much earlier, than during the period of her turmoil. Father still hadn't succeeded in finding permanent help, and Emily's endless duties around the house taxed her limited strength.

In spite of it all, she told me that she had resumed corresponding with Higginson. He had been wounded while commanding his Negro regiment and had moved with his wife to a boardinghouse in Newport to recover. "I wrote him about Carlo," Emily said.

I was glad the correspondence had been resumed. With Sue still out of favor so far as the poems were concerned, Emily needed a confidant, an adviser.

And then a strange thing happened. Who should move into the same boardinghouse with the Higginsons but . . . Helen Fiske Hunt! At the time I was unaware that she was interested in taking up writing as a profession. Had I known, I wouldn't have thought the move such a coincidence.

Life in Amherst went on pretty much as usual. I was working hard to interest the parish in building a new church. Emerson came for a series of lectures, and Sue and I entertained him. Horace Greeley delivered a lecture on Self-Made Men. Ned was ill, and then Ned was well again, running to the homestead to see his devoted aunts and Grandma. Emily was always regaling me with his latest amusing saying. "Ned says that the clock purrs and the kitten ticks, Austin!"

When Ned was five years old, our daughter was born. We named her after Sue's sister Martha, and from the beginning we called her Mattie.

Vinnie, who was like mercury as far as Sue was concerned, was in a huff with Sue at the time and didn't deign to come over to see her new niece until the second week. But Emily sent a note immediately and in a day or two tiptoed over for a peek.

About this time we had a change of preachers. The coming of Rev. Jonathan Jenkins made a big difference in my life. He was about my age, good-natured, intelligent, with a fine sense of humor. From the first Sue and I liked both him and his wife, and we spent a great deal of time together at their house or ours. He agreed with me that a new stone church was needed. Together we bent our energies toward it, full of enthusiasm and ideas.

Jonathan Jenkins was popular with the parishoners, especially so with Father. But for all the new preacher's energy in meeting people and making friends, some months passed before he met Emily. He had heard about her, of course. The village was busy with talk about Squire Dickinson's talented daughter who seldom went abroad and whose poetry was like none they had ever read.

Father invited the new preacher and his wife to his annual Commencement tea, and I had a chance to introduce them to Emily. Knowing that Father depended on her, she made a special concession and put in an appearance at the tea, talking to old friends and spontaneously strewing around the flowers of her wit.

The Jenkinses were attracted to Emily, and she to them, yet she made no change in her habit of staying home from church services.

Some time later Emily greeted me with amusement when I dropped in to chat with her in the kitchen. "Do you think I am *sound*, Austin?" she asked, with a mock serious face and laughing eyes.

"Sound?"

"Oh, not in mind or body. Nothing so earthy as that. But in *soul*. Evidently Father has questions about my soul."

"You know Father's tenacity. He probably still has secret hopes you'll join the church."

Emily was enjoying herself. "He has asked your Rev. Jonathan Jenkins to examine me and see if I am sound. And what if I'm not, Austin?"

No one knew what Emily and Jonathan talked about, but they were together in the front parlor for more than an hour. The report was what I had expected, and what I hoped would pacify Father for all time: Emily's soul was sound.

The new gray stone church of my dreams was built across the street from us, with the new parsonage at the side. Emily watched the work day by day from a vantage point at the mansion, but during the building she never ventured beyond the hedge for a better view. I showed her the plans and kept her abreast of progress on the interior. It was an unpretentious church, dignified and beautiful, with a graceful spire. To Emily it was always "Austin's church."

Father made the dedication speech to an audience that overflowed the church in spite of bad weather and muddy walks. And Emily had a chance to read all about it in the *Republican* as well as in the local paper. Then one night a few weeks later she detained me as I started to leave the homestead after consulting Father on a business matter.

"Would you take me?" she asked timidly. "Would you take me across the street to see Austin's church?"

I lighted a lantern, and we started out, like children on a secret adventure. We felt very close. The street was empty, for the hour was well past bedtime for most of the good residents of Amherst. A small cool breeze carried the smell of fall on its breath and rustled the drying leaves that still clung to the trees. Overhead the sky burned with stars.

Emily, her arm linked in mine, looked up. Night had always been a favorite time with both of us. Even before we moved from the homestead, those many years ago, we knew the names of many of the stars and looked for them. Now we stood close and silent, remembering, each in his own way. One of Emily's recent poems, one I particularly liked, filled my mind. In it she spoke of twilight coming as a stranger does, with hat in hand, wondering whether to stay or go. Then . . .

> A Vastness, as a Neigbor, came,
> A Wisdom, without Face, or Name,
> A Peace, as Hemispheres at Home
> And so the Night became.

Suddenly the "peace as hemispheres at home" swept over me, and I forgot about the little irritations that had seemed recently to make my world a drum.

"The spire is beautiful, Austin," Emily whispered.

"Shall we go in?"

Before Emily could answer, we heard the sound of wheels and hoofs. She turned to flee. "No, no. Not now." We never went again.

Before the service on Sundays Emily often sent Vinnie over with flowers for the altar and little bouquets for the pews of favorite friends, but Emily herself never entered the church. Not having expected her to, I was not disappointed.

Along about this time Father succeeded in finding an attractive Irish girl of twenty-one for permanent household help. Except for occasional sputterings about Vinnie's numerous cats, Maggie Maher fitted into life at the homestead like a bee into a flower. We all liked her and her delightful accent and hoped she would stay forever.

During these years Emily continued to send an occasional poem to Sue, and one of them unwittingly caused some unpleasant words between Sue and me. She read it aloud to me one morning when I was feeling depressed and lonely. My marriage hadn't worked out as I had hoped it would, and Sue and I were drifting further apart with every year that passed. I had been brooding over it when Sue started to read:

> There is another Loneliness
> That many die without—

The words gave me a start. This was the loneliness Emily had talked about the evening I went to chide her for not seeing Samuel Bowles. I pulled my mind back quickly to hear the rest of it.

> Not want of friend occasions it
> Or circumstance of Lot
>
> But nature, sometimes, sometimes thought
> And whoso it befall
> Is richer than could be revealed
> By mortal numeral—

"I only wish I could feel that other loneliness Emily knows so well," Sue mused. "I know all about the kind that *want of friend* occasions."

Was Sue referring to me? Was she referring to our marriage? In any event I thought the remark uncalled-for under the circumstances. I was the one who had been feeling lonesome . . . for the Sue I thought I loved years before. I blurted out, "I wasn't so far wrong, Sue, about something I wrote your sister Mattie way back before our engagement was announced."

Sue arched her eyebrows in the exasperating way she had.

"I said it was strange that you and I had chosen to love each other, because both of us were so easily miffed and so inclined to be pert. I saw then that we two could love well, or hate well."

"You weren't the only one who had doubts, Austin. And you needn't think you were. I even wrote you about them, if you remember."

I'd forgotten, and the sudden rush of memory rubbed salt into my wounds. "Why didn't one of us have the sense to act on our doubts?" I demanded, heedless of the scorn and anger I knew would be unleashed.

Such scenes never got us anywhere, and I schooled myself to avoid them, especially when the children were within earshot. I couldn't bear the thought of having them grow up in a quarreling household.

Besides, I had Emily and Vin to think about. Vinnie's affection for Sue had worn thin years before, and she was inclined to be highly critical of her. Whenever she was aware of a rift between Sue and me, Vinnie wasn't averse to giving Sue a piece of her mind.

Emily felt helpless, almost torn in two, when she sensed dissension between Sue and me or between our two households. So I tried to steel myself to maintain a dignified silence whatever the provocation. I knew that, in spite of everything, Emily felt a very real affection for Sue, and Sue for Emily; they had value for each other. I determined not to let my little irritations interfere. In time I came to get a certain satisfaction out of controlling my quick temper for the good of both households.

CHAPTER 12

THE BIG EVENT of the year 1870 for Emily, a few months before her fortieth birthday, was a visit from Thomas Wentworth Higginson. As soon as she knew that his busy schedule would permit a stopover in Amherst in mid-August, she lived in expectation of the day.

Colonel Higginson made his call in the afternoon, and that evening I talked to Emily about him after the others had retired. As usual Sue was away for the summer, with the children and their nursemaid, and I spent much of my time at the other house.

"Sue will be devastated to have missed him," I said. "He's such an idol of hers. What's he like, Emily?"

"Not a man at the head of a regiment. A man with

a quill. A poet's hand took the two lilies I offered as my introduction. He is a gentle visitor, Austin."

"Easy to talk with?"

"I was frightened at first. Never seeing strangers, I hardly knew what to say. So I asked him to talk till I felt more secure. His manner reassured me. We talked books."

"I wish I could have heard."

"I told him that when my eyes couldn't see, I was comforted to think I could easily get someone to read me the few real books that live."

"Shakespeare? The Bible?"

She nodded. "I told him about the lonely and rigorous books Father reads. And we talked about poetry. I tried to define it for him."

"How could you?"

"I said for me there were two ways, only two ways to recognize it. If a poem makes me feel too cold to be warmed by any fire, I know it is poetry. If it seems to take the top of my head off, that, too, is poetry."

I thought of some of the things Emily had written. "Safe in their alabaster chambers" chilled me to the bone. The sunlight "blazing in gold, and quenching in purple" excited me. "Yes, that is poetry," I agreed.

"Before he left, he asked me a strange question." Emily seemed amused at the recollection. "He asked if I never felt a lack because of never going away from home and never seeing visitors."

"And you told him . . . ?"

"I told him I never had the slightest thought of missing anything. And I wished I might have expressed myself more strongly, Austin. He didn't seem to understand. But on most things we stood hand in hand. He is coming again sometime, he says. Not too long away, I hope."

Higginson did visit Emily again a few years later, when he was in Amherst to deliver an evening lecture. Sue and I attended his lecture, an argument in favor of women's suffrage, a cause which Sue fervently supported. But Emily had little to say about her visit with Higginson beyond stating that they met as old friends.

Before Emily was forty, she was dressing entirely in white, except for wearing a favorite blue worsted shawl around her shoulders on chilly days. Even in winter she wore white. Was it symbolic of something or merely a passing fancy? Sue and I often wondered about it. When the habit persisted, we decided it was something more than a whim.

"It must have some special meaning for Emily," Sue said. "Something she can't talk about. Perhaps she sees some connection in her life to that part in Revelation about 'he that overcometh shall be clothed in white raiment.'" She shrugged. "We'll probably never know."

We never did find out. But whatever the reason for it, white seemed singularly appropriate for Emily.

Sue and I weren't the only ones wondering about Emily. Ned came to me one day, a troubled ten-year-old.

"What shall I say, Papa? They're always asking me about Aunt Emily."

"Who's asking?"

"The boys at school, and some of the girls, too. And sometimes even grown-up people I don't really know."

"What are they asking?"

"Why does Aunt Emily dress in white all the time? Why doesn't she go anywhere? Why doesn't she get married? There's nothing wrong with Aunt Emily, is there, Papa?"

I knew how the gossips of Amherst, full of insidious conjectures, liked to talk about Emily and her independent ways. But that Ned's classmates should pester him with questions made me boil. I tried to control my voice. "There's nothing wrong with your Aunt Emily except that she has more talent in her little finger than most people have in their whole hand."

"They ask Mattie, too, and it makes her cry. 'Did' Jenkins says I ought to fight. Only you won't let me fight. Aunt Emily's our best friend . . . and I don't know what to answer."

I fumed inwardly. Why couldn't people leave her alone? She wasn't the first unmarried woman to lead a retired life. With a whole world of the mind to explore, she was happy, happier than most women in Amherst. Even the mere sense of living was joy enough for her . . . she said so many times. And if she chose to dress in white, why shouldn't she? Why these intrusions into her privacy? Why these prying questions about her as if she were living on crumbs, when she was the one who actually lived on the whole loaf while the rest of us pecked at the crumbs?

"Tell them you don't know, Ned," I cried. "When

they ask questions, just say you don't know. Tell Mattie to say, that, too. You don't know . . . you don't *know*." In spite of myself I found that I was shouting.

"That's exactly what 'Did' said we should say."

"Did" Jenkins was the constant companion of Mattie and Ned, just as her parents were Sue's and my constant companions. The children spent hours playing together in the big yard between us and the mansion, and in the stable and oak grove and around the woodpiles. I knew that Emily was their champion, even their fellow-conspirator, in whatever they wanted to do. I watched it all, unobserved, one day when I was recuperating from an attack of malaria.

My lounge chair was on the east side of the house where I could sit and read, partly shaded by the lilac bushes. Through a gap in the green, I could look up at the two west windows of Emily's room. Sprawling there, half-lazy, half-reading, I saw Ned and Mattie and "Did" approaching stealthily in single file across the lawn and taking a position beneath Emily's windows.

I wondered what they were up to. With the kitchen ell on the far side of the house, they were out of sight of the quick eyes of Vin and Maggie. They never worried about the indulgent eyes of Emily or Grandma Dickinson.

Quietly they began to throw something at Emily's windows. I sat up, suddenly alert, staring through a larger peephole, worried lest the rascals were throwing forbidden stones. I was ready to call out, but then I saw that the "stones" acted more like old and weathered pine cones. Only Ned's came anywhere near Emily's windows. One caught her attention, and in a moment she appeared, waving her white arms in a sort of sign language.

The children stood quietly waiting, with uplifted faces. Emily disappeared for a few minutes. When she came again, she opened the window and ceremoniously let down a wicker basket on a knotted cord. The children hovered over it, filling their pockets. Then they waved their thanks and stole away like Indians to green caves of shrubbery where they could feast undisturbed. Emily pulled up the basket and closed the window.

What had she sent down? Gingerbread? Freshly-baked cookies? A poem tied to a little parcel of raisins? I smiled. No wonder Ned called Aunt Emily their best friend.

The thought of raisins made me lie back in my chair and dream. Funny how little things in the past stand out. That time when Ned was four years old, for instance. He'd been over at the mansion visiting his Grandma and doting aunts, and he forgot to take his coat when he came home. That evening when the stable-boy brought the milk, he brought Ned's coat, decorated by Emily. She had pinned down the velvet pockets with a card on each saying *Come In* and *Knock*. Ned was entranced. He found raisins under *Come In* and nuts under *Knock*.

And there was the time he forgot his rubber boots. Emily sent them back on a silver tray, filled with flowers that spilled over the tops.

Those were pleasant memories, but they made me sigh. I had hoped that the children would bring Sue and me close together, the way we had been the first years of our marriage. But it hadn't worked out like that. Except on rare occasions, Ned and Mattie seemed to be *Sue's* children, strangers to me. They went with her on long summer vacations; she planned their lives, drew them to herself, and was overindulgent. How often I felt like an outsider in my own home!

Across the yard at the mansion Father still held the reins firmly in his hands, with Mother ever content to be in second place. Not so with Sue. Never a back seat for Sue. I often wondered how she would act if she had Emily's talent for writing. She wouldn't hide behind anonymity, that was certain.

Emily continued to go her way quietly and happily, finding joy in little things that most of us overlook. She had no feeling of envy for friends who had their writings published. Our old friend, Emily Fowler Ford, having raised a family, was writing poems and having them published. Helen Fiske Hunt was writing poetry, too, with considerable success. Somehow I never thought of Helen writing poetry. Romantic novels seemed more in her line, like the tales she had regaled Ned Hitchcock and me with the day she invited herself to gather greens with us.

About this time another new literary magazine put in an appearance, with our old friend Dr. Holland of the *Springfield Republican* as editor. The first issue of *Scribner's Monthly* came out in November, 1870, a strong competitor of *Harper's* and the *Atlantic*.

On Sue's fortieth birthday that year, Vinnie gave her a copy of Helen Hunt's new book of poems. Emily was full of praise, but it seemed not to occur to her to wish that she, too, might have a book published. Her mind was on bigger things. "Oh Matchless Earth—We underrate the chance to dwell in Thee," she was writing to Sue at this time.

Father took sick that winter, and Emily devoted all her time to waiting on him. The thought that he might die oppressed her. When I pointed out that he had a constitution of iron, she answered, "But even iron rusts, Austin."

Another time she told me that the sight of his lonesome face all day was almost more than she could bear. "He never *played*, you know. He never knew how. Poor Father, he was always so straight, and now he leans." Her anxiety for him was really anguish, and I feared she would break under the strain.

When Samuel Bowles visited us in March, he was shocked by Father's appearance. "What a winter it must have been for him!" Bowles explained.

"And for Emily, too," I answered. "You know how she has always felt about Father being a tower of strength. In spite of her disagreements with him, no one could take his place."

"And speaking of Emily," Bowles said, "can't we get her to Boston somehow? She mentioned to me once that Colonel Higginson would like to introduce her to some of his literary friends. And why not? She shouldn't withdraw from the world and lose touch."

"It's not really withdrawal, Sam. Emily keeps up with things. She reads your paper every day and knows what's happening in the world. You've heard the penetrating questions she asks about people and current affairs."

"I still deplore it, Austin. Never going beyond the hedge any more."

"You're a different type," I objected. "That's all. Yours is a world of people, of activity. Emily makes a world of a gentian. Besides, if she is going to keep on writing, she hasn't time for social things. Life is choices, you know. Emily has made hers, and I respect it."

Father recovered slowly. Not until late spring was he back in the office, eager to make up for lost time.

That year both Father and I came in for some recognition that was highly gratifying to Emily. An article appeared in the *Republican*, congratulating me on my taste and judgment in helping to plan the new buildings for the College and in overseeing the landscaping of the grounds. "Well done, Austin," was all Father said, but Emily told me how proudly he brought home the paper and asked her to read the article aloud, not once, but twice.

In the fall Father was one of the first to be written up in the Amherst *Record's* series of articles about its leading citizens. Emily clipped the piece and put it in the soup tureen. The article said the name of Dickinson was so identified with everything that belonged to Amherst that any attempt to speak of town history would be impossible without that name appearing the most prominent.

After his illness, Father's load of responsibilities seemed to weigh on him. Although he regained his strength, he tired easily. He began to look for ways to enjoy more leisure at home. Reluctantly he resigned as treasurer of the College in 1872, after having served for thirty-seven years. The College had been deep in debt when he took over the finances, and now it was worth half a million dollars. Later, elected by the board of trustees, I took his place as treasurer.

That was the year Abby Wood, Mrs. Daniel Bliss, returned from Syria with her two boys, to put them in school in Amherst. For weeks ahead of time Luke Sweetser and his wife bustled about in anticipation. Abby and Daniel Bliss had made a name for themselves as missionary educators, and he had founded the Syrian Protestant College.

"Imagine seeing Abby again!" Vinnie exclaimed one August evening when I was at the homestead. She had called on Abby's aunt, Mrs. Sweetser, that afternoon. "I wonder what she looks like. She's your age, isn't she, Emily? Forty-two. Think of her having two boys old enough to go to high school. Well, maybe Howard isn't *quite* old enough, but Fred is."

"They'll go on and get their degrees at the College, no doubt," I said. "And it wasn't so long ago that you girls had your playhouse in the grove. Are the boys going to stay at Sweetsers'?"

181

"Nothing's really definite until they get here, but Mrs. Sweetser wants them to," Vinnie replied. "She says Fred is a talented pianist."

Emily showed interest. "Is he? He must take after Abby. I can still see her white hands fluttering over the keys."

Both Vinnie and I assumed that Emily would emerge from her retirement long enough to have a good old-fashioned visit with Abby Wood Bliss. But a week or so after the Blisses arrived, Abby appeared at the office to discuss some business matters with me . . . and to ask about Emily.

"What's come over Emily, Austin? She's so evasive about seeing me."

"It's not a pose, I assure you, Abby. It's just that Emily has been retiring more and more from the world over a period of years. She has been writing. No one knows how much. But we've had some wonderful and unusual poems from her. Sue thinks she has great talent. Somehow she sort of lives in a different world from the rest of us."

Abby nodded good-naturedly. "And she has every right to. I've been hearing things, of course, Austin. I suppose it's only natural when one lives an . . . well, an unconventional sort of life. But I thought Emily would want to renew our friendship. It seems there are any number of preliminaries attendant on such a visit, though."

"It's diffidence mainly. Emily always had a timid streak, you remember. It's been exaggerated with the

182

years. Now she's so afraid she won't know what to *say*, it withers her. She's just plain afraid to meet people, I think."

"Poor darling Emily! I understand, and I won't bother her. Do give her my love, won't you? Tell her I have nothing but the fondest memories of our childhood friendship; that I've forgotten nothing, nothing of my constant delight in her. And tell her I'd like to have her hear Fred play the piano sometime."

I gave Emily the messages. "She was so understanding," I said. "She doesn't hold it against you for a moment that you aren't opening your arms to her."

That broke Emily down. She rose above her timidity, saw Abby as an old friend, and delighted in the visit.

Meanwhile Father's resolution to take things easier began to evaporate, much to Emily's distress. He was back in politics again, running on the Republican ticket for the state legislature.

"He doesn't remember how ill he was," Emily moaned. "Oh, Austin, I hope he won't be elected."

But he was elected by almost two-thirds of the votes cast.

Emily couldn't understand the lure of politics. "Why does he do it when he hates so to be away from home?" she asked. "He's seventy years old, almost seventy-one. What if he takes sick off there alone in Boston?"

I tried to assure her that it would be good for him to have a chance to work for a new railroad to Amherst. Lack of traffic to support the line from Belchertown had caused it to fail, and the stockholders had lost all their money. Father was heartsick over it. Now he was fired with enthusiasm to bring in an east-west line that would run through better territory in the central part of the state. "If Father can talk the legislature into building a tunnel to complete the new railroad, it will do wonders for him," I pointed out.

"Yes, Austin. I must keep remembering that."

A few days after his seventy-first birthday on New Year's Day, 1874, Father left for Boston, full of plans for speeches he intended to make before the legislature. He was in good health and spirits. As usual he urged us to send him a note every morning so he would know how we all were.

He made it a point to come home as often as he could. On one visit, in April, he stayed home longer than he expected because he was ill. Emily hovered over him. "Think, Austin," she said to me, shuddering, "it might have happened in Boston, in a hotel room!"

"He'll be up and around again in a few days," I told her. "I had a talk with Dr. Smith yesterday. Don't worry."

Before the week was out, Father was well enough to go back to Boston, and Emily was her joyous self again. She beckoned me to a corner of the kitchen to share her amusement. An April snowstorm had kept Father from returning to Boston for a day or two.

"You should have seen him this morning," Emily said. "There were those mistaken birds who had come home too soon, sitting by the kitchen door, whimpering about being cold and hungry and frightened. Father went out to the barn in his slippers, along the little path, and brought back a breakfast of grain. And how do you think he scattered it?" Her voice dropped to a tender whisper. "He stood behind the door, Austin, for fear he would embarrass them."

Father came home again the latter part of May to attend a citizen's relief meeting, after a terrible spring flood had swept through three of our Hampshire County villages. Before going back to Boston, he came over to see Ned who was ill again. Apprehensively Father told us to be sure to telegraph him if Ned grew worse. Ned's recovery, he said, was more important to him than all the lawmaking in the Legislature.

The second week in June, when he came to Amherst for a long week-end, Father brought Emily two books which delighted her—one by Theodore Parker and the other by her beloved George Eliot. I went over to the mansion late Sunday afternoon to visit and talk over some business matters with Father. I found him and Emily alone in the parlor, Emily at the piano singing, "Rest from thy loved employ."

"This is the kind of day I would like never to end," Father said as he greeted me.

Emily turned from the piano. "The concert is over. With the afternoon withdrawing, the heat will be withdrawing, too. What could be a better time for you to show Father how the new planting is thriving at the College, Austin?"

It was indeed a beautiful time of day for a walk. And I shall never forget that hour with Father, any more than Emily ever forgot her time alone with him in the parlor.

Early the next morning Father went back to Boston, to be on hand to speak in favor of the railroad tunnel. When I said good-by, I urged him not to overexert himself in the unseasonably warm weather we were having, knowing full well that, heat or no heat, he would speak as ardently as he could to promote the new railroad line.

Two days afterward, late in the afternoon, a boy came to the Evergreens with a dispatch. Father had suffered a stroke! After addressing the House in the heat of noonday, he had gone back to his hotel and eaten dinner. He was stricken almost immediately afterward and was very ill.

I dashed over to the mansion. Mother, Emily, and Vin were at the supper table.

"It's Father!" Emily gasped when she saw my face. "It's Father!"

Mother looked from her to me. She could not speak.

"What *is* it, Austin?" Vinnie pressed.

I read them the dispatch. "Vinnie and I must go to Boston at once. The train has already left. We'll have to take horses to make another connection."

"Alone, at his hotel!" Emily said in an awed voice.

I rushed off to see about the horses and to put a few things into my grip. Soon a boy appeared with another dispatch. Trembling, I read the news that Father was dead.

We were all stunned beyond words.

Father was buried on Ned's thirteenth birthday. I was too engulfed in grief even to realize that the boy was having a birthday. Mother and Emily and Vinnie were groping their way through a nightmare that seemed to have no end.

On the afternoon of the funeral, stores closed in the village and townsfolk crowded into the mansion and overflowed the lawn. The odor of flowers hung heavy on the warm June air. We of the family—except Emily— sat in the library during the short service of a hymn, a reading from the Scriptures, and a prayer by Rev. Jenkins. Emily stayed in her room, and I envied her. No one expected her to appear. The rest of us moved like puppets through the conventions of a funeral.

Appreciative articles about Father came out in Amherst and Northampton papers, and Samuel Bowles ran a long obituary in the *Republican*. Rev. Jenkins preached a sermon on him, making a parallel with the life of Samuel, the prophet. In a short time the outward marks of respect were over, but we Dickinsons felt the wrench of Father's passing for a long time to come. Mother slumped, never to regain her strength. Emily's withdrawal from the world became complete.

That summer and fall after Father's death the world seemed very much like a drum. People made a great to-do about inconsequential matters, I thought, like the authorship of the Saxe Holm stories which had been appearing in *Scribner's Monthly*. The papers and literary magazines conjectured about who was hiding behind the name Saxe Holm. Various authors were suggested from time to time, prominent among them our friend, Helen Fiske Hunt. She might well have written the stories, but I felt impatient with the amount of attention the guessing game evoked. What concerned me more, and Sue, too, was the effect of Father's death on Emily's writing. Would her grief dry up her source of inspiration?

For weeks and months no poem came across the lawn to Sue; at least none that Sue told me about. I finally asked her if Emily had given up writing.

"She keeps wondering where Father has gone," I said. "She keeps asking *what kind* he has become."

"She has sent me a few short notes, Austin, and flowers. But no poems."

"Those last two books Father brought her, Sue, still lie unread. She can't bear to open them. She says she would like to send them to Colonel Higginson."

Sue shook her head sadly. "You and Emily were so tied to your Father. Tied in different ways, but nevertheless tied."

Before the year was out, a poem of twelve lines came to our house. I reread the ending many times:

> To die is not to go—
> On Doom's consummate Chart
> No Territory new is staked—
> Remain thou as thou art.

Whom could she be thinking of but Father? "To die is not to go."

The next day Emily sent an alternative reading for the second stanza, and Sue and I liked it better than the first. Sue pinned it to her workbox, and I often stopped to read it, finding comfort in the words:

> Eternity will be
> Velocity or Pause
> Precisely as the Candidate
> Preliminary was—

CHAPTER *13*

WE ALL found it hard to adjust to life without Father. At every turn we were reminded of him. When spring came, Emily told me that the birds Father had rescued from the snowstorm were back, trifling in his trees. "And," she added, "when Vinnie went with pussy willows yesterday, she even found them frolicking at his grave."

But even with missing Father, Emily was again finding some of her irrepressible joy in living. I came upon her in the garden one morning in late March, the spring after Father died, as she tripped about looking for the first buds and blossoms. "Oh, Austin," she cried, "infinite March is here. I heard a bluebird, and I'm standing on my head." She felt under her shawl in the pocket of her dress for a piece of wrapping paper and handed it to me. "Read it aloud so I can hear how it sounds before I send it to Sue."

I read it through silently first, to be sure I could make out the writing. Then I read aloud:

> A little Madness in the Spring
> Is wholesome even for the King,
> But God be with the Clown—
> Who ponders this tremendous scene—
> This whole Experiment of Green—
> As if it were his own!

"I'm not sure of it yet, Austin. I've tried a number of words in place of *experiment of green*. Turn over the paper and you'll see."

I was surprised at the number of possibilities she had thought of: *sudden legacy of Green, fair Apocalypse of Green, gay, bright, fleet, sweet, quick, whole, This whole Apocalypse of Green, experience, Astonishment, Periphery, wild experiment, Experiment.*

"Does *sudden legacy of green* express the thought better?" she wanted to know.

I thought it good, but no better than *experiment of green*, and she let it stand at that.

She was to be envied, I thought. To be able to feel the madness of spring during her grief, after the heyday of youth was over, and to have the madness rich with overtones! Yes, she was to be envied.

Then in June another blow struck. Exactly a year

from the evening Father died, Mother suffered a stroke that left her paralyzed. I always thought the affliction was brought on by her unceasing grief for Father. With his going, she seemed to lose her will to live.

Now Emily and Vin and Maggie had a permanent invalid to care for. But strangely enough, Mother's helplessness brought Emily closer to her than ever before. Emily's attention had always been centered on Father. But now that Mother needed her, Emily responded with a depth of affection and compassion that surprised the rest of us.

All was not sadness that summer of '75. On the last night of July a third child was born to Sue and me—a son. We named him Thomas Gilbert, after Sue's father, as Ned had been named after mine; but from the first we called him Gib for short. Gib of the blond hair and blue eyes! Almost at once he proved a blessing to all of us. Sue and I had not felt so close in years as when we admired our healthy, happy boy.

Everyone loved Gib. Unwittingly he smoothed relations between Sue and Vinnie, relations that had been strained to the breaking point for a long time. Gib's winning smile and beguiling ways melted dissension as sun melts snow. Hardly a rift marred Emily's and Sue's affection for each other after Gib came to live with us.

As for me, I had a special love for Gib that I had never felt for Ned or Mattie. He was a rare spirit.

Poor Father! He never knew Gib. How he would have rejoiced in his dignified way that there was another Dickinson to carry on the name. Ned's frequent illnesses had preyed on Father's mind, although he never spoke of them, as a danger to the continuity of the line. With Gib's birth, he would have been reassured. Strange, that was something that mattered little to Emily.

I was instrumental that fall in having Judge Lord and his wife spend a week at the homestead for pleasure intermingled with business. With Mother ill and paralyzed, I was afraid that she might go like Father, without a will. I wanted to make sure that she would leave everything to the girls. I already had more than my share—the Evergreens, the office, and a thriving law practice. The girls must have the mansion and Father's investments. Judge Lord, old friend of the family that he was, seemed the ideal person to write Mother's will, and Emily's and Vin's, too.

That week with the Lords meant a great deal to Emily. I could see her open up in a way that she hadn't for months, with the Judge's keen mind to rise to. The two of them talked books for hours on end, particularly Shakespeare, while Vinnie and Mrs. Lord recalled the old days when Vin was at Ipswich Seminary close to the Lord's protective eyes.

One of the high points of Emily's life came a few months later . . . not with anything that happened, but with five short words in a letter from Colorado. Emily never showed me the letter, nor did she tell me the words, but she told them timidly to Sue, and Sue told them to me, and we both glowed with satisfaction.

The letter came from Helen Fiske Hunt. She had

moved to Colorado for her health, and there she had married again and was now Helen Hunt Jackson. Indirectly through Colonel Higginson she had known that Emily was writing poetry. And she herself had been writing in earnest under his guidance and encouragement ever since she had stayed at the Newport boardinghouse where he lived with his wife. Like Emily, Helen preferred anonymity, usually writing under the initials H. H. But unlike Emily, she wanted publication. Her book reviews and travel articles had been appearing in the literary magazines. And, of course, we read the Saxe Holm stories, which many readers were sure came from Helen's pen.

When her book of poems appeared, Emily had read it eagerly. "Her poems are strong, Austin," she told me. "I think they're stronger than any written by women since Mrs. Browning." Then quickly she added, "With the exception of George Eliot. But still stronger than any written by American women."

All in all, Emily regarded Helen of Colorado as one of the leading writers of verse in the United States, man or woman. From no one could words of praise have meant more to Emily. So when Helen wrote her in March, 1876, "You are a great poet," those five words set the year apart for Emily.

"There was more in the letter," Sue said. "Helen wrote that she had a little notebook in which she kept a few of Emily's poems, probably some given her over the years by Colonel Higginson. She said she kept them although she knew them by heart—and that was more than she could say for her own verses. But there was one thing that didn't please Emily."

"About publication?" I ventured.

Sue nodded. "She said Emily was wrong not to sing so others could hear."

"And Emily said?"

"Something about publication being the auction of the mind of man."

"Well, in a way it is!" I exclaimed, jumping to Emily's defense. "We Dickinsons . . ."

"Yes, I know," Sue finished impatiently, "we Dickinsons are independent."

"And none more independent than Sue," I remarked, amused at her tartness. How well I remembered that first Christmas after our marriage when Sue put up laurel wreaths to decorate the windows, scandalizing the Puritan townsfolk with their prejudice against Christmas ornaments and display. But Sue never yielded an inch. The wreaths stayed up all during the holidays.

When Helen of Colorado came to Amherst with her husband for a short visit in October that year, Emily broke her rule of solitude and agreed to see them. Sue saw the carriage stop in front of the mansion and a fashionably-dressed woman on the arm of her husband walk up the steps and through the gate to the portico. The carriage waited. About an hour later it was gone.

The next time I saw Emily I asked how she had enjoyed the visit.

"She's grown very handsome, Austin."

"I thought so, too, when I saw her at Commencement five or six years ago. And she knows how to dress. And who would have thought that she would become so famous?"

"She's vivid and talks brilliantly, but . . ." Emily hesitated.

"Where does she want you to publish a poem this time?" I teased.

"In the most nameless of publications," came the quick reply. She told me that Helen had come east to supervise the publication of her new novel, *Mercy Philbrick's Choice*, the first book in a "No-Name Series." Each book in the series was to be published anonymously, and readers were to try to guess the author. "She doesn't know how much we'll like *Mercy Philbrick*," Emily said. "It's set in Amherst, and there are certain similarities to living persons."

"Dangerous business. But of course, it will be anonymous."

Emily gave me a quizzical look. "She says some readers may even think *I* had a hand in it."

"Is that what she came to see you about? To give you fair warning?"

Emily shook her head. "There's to be another book in the No-Name Series that Helen is particularly interested in—an anthology of poetry, a masque of poets. She wants me to have a poem in the book. But of course, I couldn't."

It was with something of a shock that Sue and I read *Mercy Philbrick's Choice* when it came out, even though we had been forewarned. Who could the heroine be but a combination of Emily Dickinson and Helen Hunt Jackson? Mercy Philbrick hid herself from callers. She had an ailing mother who was quite helpless. In her young days she had a dear friend who reminded me strongly of Newton, and later an older friend who might have been Dr. Wadsworth. On the other hand, like Helen Hunt, the heroine before her second marriage was a widow who became famous as a poet. The plot was different enough to make the story seem fictitious. Emily found it all highly amusing.

My health was a great worry to Emily that winter when I suffered the most severe attack of malaria I ever had. She feared I would die.

As if that wasn't enough, our close and loved friend, Jonathan Jenkins, decided to resign his pastorate. Continual dissension in the congregation had discouraged him. So when a call came from Pittsfield, he accepted it. This blow on top of my debilitating fever and chills was almost too much for me. Then, while I was still recuperating, Ned became suddenly and disturbingly ill, as if taken with fits. Sue and I had never been so alarmed. When he recovered a few days later, we felt drained of strength and perspective.

Emily's butterfly and her infectious excitement over it helped restore my equilibrium.

When putting her garden to bed in the fall, Emily had found a chrysalis encased in a hard protective covering, attached to a twig by strong threads of silk. Carefully she had carried the twig into the conservatory and placed it among her plants, where she watched it attentively all winter.

Then one Sunday morning in March, when the snow seemed to jump up and down with dazzling sunlight, Maggie hurried over with a note from Emily. We must all come, quietly, one by one, to see the chiffon surprise. There was an exciting breathlessness about the note. The time had come!

Ned went first and returned with the awed report that the butterfly had broken from its cocoon and was already flitting about the conservatory.

When my turn came, I carried Gib over on my shoulder. He was just beginning to talk.

"We're going to see a big surprise that came out of a tiny house," I told him. "A tiny house Aunt Emily found."

Emily ushered us into the conservatory on tiptoe. "There!" she whispered, pointing to a vine near the windows. A bright swallowtail was clinging to one of the leaves.

"Where's the little house?" asked Gib.

In a moment the butterfly rose and fluttered to Emily's big daphne odora. The sight of it raised my spirits. Here was spring while snow still covered the world outside the window. Here was . . . one might almost call it resurrection. Life. Hope.

"Where's the little house?" Gib persisted.

Emily showed him the small brown case clinging to the twig, still attached by silken threads around its middle. "You see, he came out the door at the top. He opened it all by himself. And then he unpacked his wings and flew away."

Emily was always unpacking a surprise, I thought, as I carried Gib back across the snowy path. Somehow she always found spring before winter disappeared around the corner. I constantly marveled at the way she kept up her enthusiasm and interest in spite of her self-inflicted imprisonment and her household cares.

Her sense of humor, her quick wit, never deserted her. One evening a strange tan cat ducked between my feet in the back hall and almost upset me.

"Who's that wild creature endangering a man's life?" I demanded of Emily in the kitchen.

"That's Vinnie's new pussy. She catches a mouse an hour, Austin; so I call her Minute Hand."

Another time I heard Vinnie sputtering over a letter she had been reading to Emily, who was arranging flowers for the sideboard.

"You look like a thundercloud, Vin," I said.

She tossed her head. "Who wouldn't! As if we don't have enough to do without putting up with Aunt Libby again . . . even if Emily does find her *distinctive*."

"Distinctive? Aunt Libby?"

"Why yes, Austin," Emily said. "She's our only male relative on the female side, isn't she? The trees will stand at attention when they hear her boots thumping into Amherst. I fear they'll bear crockery instead of fruit. And I've no doubt she'll starch my geraniums before she leaves."

Occasional pleasant breaks in the routine swept Emily to "another spot," as she expressed it, from which she returned newer. Sometimes young friends of Vin's from the church came to play and sing, and Emily listened from her room upstairs. Her special pleasure came when Fred Bliss, Abby's son, played Beethoven and Chopin and Schumann and Schubert in the empty parlor. I doubt if he ever saw Emily. But her notes of appreciation must have meant a great deal to him, for he played willingly and often.

Another pleasure she looked forward to was an occasional visit from Samuel Bowles that pointed up her lively correspondence with him. And she always enjoyed the overnight visits of Judge and Mrs. Lord. The Hollands, too, meant a great deal to her, both their visits and her correspondence with them, especially with Mrs. Holland, whom she called "Sister." It seemed to me all along that Emily's isolation was purely physical, which is why it never struck me as being eccentric. Mentally she more than kept in touch with her close friends—through her letters and theirs she took an active part in their lives and thoughts.

In many ways, though, those years of the late 1870's were years that tried our souls. Shortly before Christmas the year Emily turned forty-seven, Mrs. Lord died. She was beautiful to look at and intelligent to talk to, and kindly in her judgment of people. I couldn't help wondering if her death would change Judge Lord's habit of visiting us often. Emily would miss her intellectual bouts with him.

A month after Mrs. Lord's death another shock plunged both households into darkness. Samuel Bowles succumbed to an illness of long standing. He was only fifty-two, three years older than I was. For thirty-five years he had been building up the *Springfield Republican*, giving it his sparkle and vivacity, his vitality and drive. Often he worked far into the night. Ill health nagged at him for years before he finally burned out from exhaustion and overwork.

And then in June of '78, Mother broke her hip. Her invalidism was now complete. Except for being lifted into an easy chair, she would never leave her bed again.

How did Emily, I wondered, have the time or the heart to keep up with her writing and reading in the midst of the sorrows that befell us? Sue showed me nothing that came from the other house at this time, and, as we were drifting apart again, I hesitated to ask. And so I was relieved when Mattie came home from a visit with "Did" Jenkins in Pittsfield to hear that Emily had written to her and "Did."

"What did she say, Mattie?"

"Oh, she hoped we were having a good time. And she called us rascals and sent her love. She even ended with a poem."

I pricked up my ears. "A poem for rascals?"

"It was only four lines, and I didn't much understand the last two, so I only remember the first two:

Who has not found the Heaven—below—
Will fail of it above . . .

Do you think it's true, Papa?"

The lines burned in my mind. Only with Gib . . .
only with Gib did I seem to be finding the heaven
below. "If it's true, Mattie," I answered slowly, "it's a
fearful thought." Who . . . who in our two households,
in all of Amherst, was finding heaven below? Probably
only Emily, about whom there was so much gossip and
conjecture. Emily, the Myth. Emily, the Recluse. Yet
Emily, emerging from shadows that engulfed the rest of
us.

Three or four months after Mother broke her hip,
Helen of Colorado and her husband drove over to Amherst from Northampton, where they were visiting on
another trip East. Emily was expecting them. She never
said much about the visit, but when her poem *Success*
appeared in the Masque of Poets in the No-Name Series
toward the end of 1878, I assumed that Helen had pre-
vailed upon her to allow it to be published.

The poem was not a new one. I remembered reading
a copy sent to Sue years before. The first four of the
twelve lines appealed to me particularly:

> Success is counted sweetest
> By those who ne'er succeed.
> To comprehend a nectar
> Requires sorest need.

The editor sent a copy of the book to Emily upon
publication, and she was horrified to discover that five
changes had been made in the text.

"Must they always make changes!" she exclaimed.

"How can they be so sure they know more than the writer?"

Reviewers praised the poem as one of the most successful in the book, and one reviewer even said that if Emerson had contributed to the book, *Success* was probably the poem.

Sue and I could think of no higher praise.

CHAPTER *14*

No ONE of our generation in Amherst would ever forget the Fourth of July, 1879. We were sound asleep when bells began to ring at one o'clock in the morning.

"Just celebrating the Fourth early," I mumbled to Sue. "Probably somebody's idea of fun, to ring the bells."

Sleepily I heard her go out and come running back. "The sky's all red, Austin! There must be a fire."

Fire! I jumped out of bed. Fires had plagued Amherst for as long as I could remember. For years Father had fought for a more dependable water supply than private wells, and since his death I had carried on the fight for water to be piped from the Pelham hills. But so far nothing had been done.

Off I dashed.

The Cutler block was in flames, and the fire was spreading through the business district. An inferno raged.

Six hours later I stumbled home, wet and exhausted. Most of the able-bodied men of Amherst had carried water in bucket brigades to help the hook-and-ladder volunteers fight the fire. For a while it had looked as if the whole town might go. Never had I put in such a night.

Instead of turning in at my gate, I went on to the mansion. Ned would certainly keep Sue informed, but what about Emily and Vin? Had they been worried and frightened as the fire flamed through the night, brightening the sky with eerie red? And what about Mother?

Emily met me at the door. "Is anything left?" she asked. Solicitously she led me to Father's favorite old chair and called Maggie to bring hot tea.

"There's not much left of the business section," I replied. "The post office is gone, the bank, the hotel, most of the stores. At that we're lucky. If the wind had been from the southwest, all Main Street would have gone. Were you badly frightened?"

"I heard the bells. I ran to the window and saw that awful red. It was so bright, Austin, that if I'd looked toward the orchard, I could have seen a caterpillar measuring a leaf. But Vinnie came in, soft as a moccasin, and said it was only the Fourth of July."

How like Vinnie, I thought. Always trying to spare Emily!

"Vinnie and I took hands," she went on, "and slipped into Mother's room. She was asleep, with Maggie sitting beside her. Vinnie whispered something to Maggie, and Maggie said, 'Only Stebbins' barn. Only Stebbins' barn.' I could hear each crash and explosion, like chaos, but I let them deceive me. Was it awful being so close to the fire?"

"Terrible." I took a calming sip of Maggie's tea. "But it will do more than fifty committee meetings toward getting water piped from the Pelham hills."

The great fire did indeed speed up the installation of a water system for Amherst. By the following June water from the hills was running through pipes, and a celebrative stream flowed from the hydrant near the Amherst House. Soon afterward I had water piped to my house and the mansion. Emily was fascinated by the garden hose. Now she could water her flowers during the dusty dryness of summer, instead of trying to cajole Dennis, the stableman, into carrying buckets of water. She told me delightedly what a sight it was to see the birds follow the hose for a crumb of water.

Gib, too, took delight in the hose. He even squirted the trees . . . "so they can drink better, Papa."

Gib was the pride and joy of both households. At the age of three he took over the duties of messenger boy. His willing legs went back and forth, back and forth, and his pockets, I am afraid, bulged with too many rewards. He could always be sure of his grandmother's gentle love, of Maggie's blustery indulgence, of Vinnie's wavering discipline, and of Emily's pixylike delight in him.

Emily saved some of Gib's jewels to string for me when I came over inquiring after Mother's health or the state of the household. "Your beguiling urchin defended his own case in court today," she told me one summer evening when Gib was nearing his fifth birthday.

"What was he up to now?"

"Chasing Vinnie's pussy—the one who likes to sharpen claws on legs. Vinnie caught Gib in the act."

"And he had the nerve to defend his case . . . against *Vinnie?*"

"You should have heard him, Austin. Vinnie cross-examined him in her most severe legal voice: 'Weren't you chasing pussy?' Gib looked as wily as the Sphinx. 'She was chasing herself, Aunt Vinnie.' "

The rascal. I could see his teasing blue eyes.

"Vinnie pressed her case: 'But wasn't she running pretty fast?' 'Well,' said the culprit, giving his prosecutor an utterly disarming smile. 'Some slow and some fast.' Of course, he was acquitted."

Some of my closest and most joyous moments with Emily were spent talking about Gib, and the amusing things he did and said: the way he tipped his hat and carried his small cane, trying to mimic Ned; the way he shouted in the carriage to make the horses hurry; the way he appeared suddenly for no reason at all except to be assured of affection, which was always his.

We shared another source of unending amusement, Emily and I. For years we had made a game of clipping solemn nonsense from the papers and exchanging the bits with caustic or witty comments. Emily started it when I was in law school.

Several months after Jonathan Jenkins, whom I affectionately called John, had moved away with his family, Emily handed me a little item from the newspaper. It concerned a certain John Jenkins arrested in Baltimore for passing counterfeit coins.

I chuckled. The last sentence struck me as being especially funny, for John Jenkins was suspected of being employed by a gang of counterfeiters.

"What are you going to say when you send it?" I asked.

"I'll give them our sympathy," Emily replied, "and I'll ask *whom* we can trust when an old friend like the Decalogue turns his back on us."

I missed John and Sarah Jenkins more than I dared admit to myself. For some reason, in their company Sue and I were able to forget our differences. The happiest times of our married life were the ten years spent with John and his wife, in our house or in the parsonage across the street. Of course, we continued to visit back and forth after they moved to Pittsfield, but that failed to fill the gap in our lives.

On the surface we kept up a bold front. Sue's parties were still the talk of the town, though for me they became more and more mere shells of entertainment. There were more intimate social times, of course, when Judge Lord came, or when Samuel Bowles, Jr., brought friends from Springfield. One spring day he brought Frances Hodgson Burnett for luncheon. We knew her from her books and serials in *Scribner's Monthly* and *Godey's Lady's Book*, but had never met her.

Young Mrs. Burnett was charming, still very English in spite of her fifteen years in the States. During our animated conversation at the table, we were interrupted by a surprise from next door. The maid brought in from the kitchen a gift for Mrs. Burnett—a dainty bed of heartsease with a bow and one of Emily's poems resting upon it. Without putting in an appearance, Emily had added an unforgettable touch to our luncheon.

One could never be sure of Vinnie's contributions or reactions. Her good nature wobbled like the old weathervane atop the homestead barn, especially where Sue was concerned. I never knew from one month to the next whether Vin and Sue were on speaking terms. And so I was not surprised one August day to have Vinnie gloat over a secret she could dangle tantalizingly before Sue. Vin stopped in at the office while she was on a shopping expedition.

"Don't tell Sue," she warned, "but Emily had an unexpected caller last night."

"Emily!" I was surprised that none of us had seen or heard a carriage stop at the mansion, but I waited for Vin to get on with her story.

"Emily was in the conservatory putting her plants to bed when there was a knock at the door. Maggie went to open it, and I heard a deep voice."

"Vin, you vixen, don't string it out. Who was it?"

"He must have walked from the station. At least, I saw no carriage waiting when I looked later. I ran and told Emily that the gentleman with the deep voice wanted to see her."

I looked blank.

"Her clergyman from Philadelphia, Austin."

"Dr. Wadsworth!" Of course, I knew from the *Republican* that Dr. Wadsworth had long since returned to Philadelphia. He and Emily must have carried on a correspondence meaningful to them both for him to come to Amherst a second time, and for Emily to be willing to see him.

"He stayed for all of an hour," Vinnie went on. "But Emily hasn't told me a thing they talked about." She shook a finger at me. "Don't tell Sue. The less she knows, the better!"

Judge Lord was another exception to Emily's rule of no callers. After his wife died, my concern lest the Judge curtail his visits proved unfounded. I feared he might find it hard to come alone. But as it turned out, two of his wife's nieces, Abbie and Mary Farley, often came with him. They all stayed at the Inn, and the Judge spent long hours in conversation with Emily at the mansion.

I thought it only natural, since he had been Father's greatest friend, for Emily to turn to him as a pillar of strength.

But Sue had other ideas. One evening she annoyed me by blurting out, "It's disgraceful, Austin! Oh, I hadn't meant to say anything, but how can I help it? Imagine, I went over to the mansion this afternoon to bring a book to Emily, and what do you suppose I found in the parlor?"

I could think of nothing under heaven Sue might have found in the parlor to upset her. I shrugged, waiting for her to go on.

"Well, I found Emily in the arms of Judge Lord."

I knew Sue's propensity for making a good story out of a trivial incident, and it put my back up. "You make it sound shocking, Sue. It was nothing more than a fatherly embrace, you can be sure of that."

"I know a fatherly embrace when I see one," Sue retorted. "Besides, Abbie Farley says he sends very personal notes to the mansion. She doesn't approve at all . . . feels he's being disloyal to his dead wife."

"I don't care to hear any more of Abbie Farley's gossip," I said, starting to leave the room. Sue arched her eyebrows in an exasperated look, and there the matter ended.

Judge Lord continued his visits to Amherst and often was a dinner guest at our home. I constantly marveled at Sue's power to cover up her real feelings. There was no outward change in her manner toward the Judge; she was as charming and scintillating as ever.

Sue's fiftieth birthday, which came nine days after Emily's, was a trying day for her. The main object of her life, it seemed to me, was having a good time, and her popularity depended on the verve of youth. She clung to it tenaciously. On her fiftieth birthday she seemed oppressed by that horror of age that besets so many middle-aged women.

How different Emily was! On her fiftieth birthday

a few days before, I found her as light-hearted as usual when I crossed the snowy yard to wish her happiness. Far from being concerned about her age, she was delighting in the pattern of white wool branches against the gray flannel sky. She was pleased, too, that Mother had seemed to enjoy her supper more than usual.

"You know, Austin," she said with a childlike air of discovery. "We never were intimate with Mother while she was our *mother*. But how affectionate we are now that she has become our child!"

Even though Emily had no concern with age, she seemed to understand Sue's feelings, and she wrote a little poem to reassure her. Had Sue not been puzzled over the last two lines, I probably never would have seen it. She had not shared any of Emily's poems with me for months . . . though perhaps there had been none to share. In any event, on the birthday night, Sue handed me four lines:

> Birthday of but a single pang
> That there are less to come—
> Afflictive is the Adjective
> But affluent the doom—

"Does Emily mean that most of us consider age an affliction, but that it really has riches of its own?" Sue asked. "That's the best I can make out of it."

I could see no better explanation. "Emily seems to be escaping the affliction," I mused, "and pocketing the riches."

"Yes," Sue answered quickly. "She's always pocketed

more riches than the rest of us. And I'd envy her if she didn't pay such a price for them?"

"What price?"

"Why, renouncing all the pleasures that make life come alive to me."

In their way they both were right. Sue was a woman of the outer world, Emily of the inner. Somehow, although I too was enmeshed in passing events, I couldn't help feeling that Emily's way gave a depth to life that was missing from Sue's and in great measure from mine.

To help us celebrate our twenty-fifth wedding anniversary, Emily and Vin sent over some special cakes and currant wine of their own making. I didn't have to tell Emily that Sue and I were celebrating the event with mixed emotions. Emily knew that we had started out with high hopes and an idealistic picture of what marriage and a home should be. She knew of our success in outward things—a beautiful home, books, paintings, servants, high-stepping horses, and even a carriage man to drive Sue around. But she knew, too, that though children had blessed our marriage, something was lacking. Somewhere along the line something had gone wrong. Emily was keenly aware that, except for Gib, I found little happiness in the imposing house Sue called the Evergreens.

For me the best part of that anniversary came in the evening when Gib and I walked in the Dickinson meadow across the road, trying to catch fireflies. It was like the times long past when Emily and I were children at the homestead, running after fireflies before bedtime.

Fireflies always made me think of Emily, she was so like one herself—always a blink ahead.

The next day we were all shocked by the news that President Garfield had been shot by a disappointed office-seeker.

For weeks the President's life trembled on the scales, and we read the papers hopefully. Even Mother, whose mind wandered much of the time, urged Emily each morning to read about the President's condition. For two and a half months he lingered before succumbing to the bullet wound.

"Father will be so sorry," Mother said. "Where *is* Father all this time? Still in the legislature? When will he come home?"

"Tomorrow, Mama," Emily whispered. "Tomorrow with a capital letter."

About this time young David Peck Todd, an Amherst graduate, became professor of astronomy at the College and director of the observatory, and he moved to Amherst with his talented and vivacious wife. Sue and I called on them in late September, when they were just getting settled in their Pleasant Street house, and we were delighted with them both.

On our way home Sue quoted the old saying about one door closing and another opening. "Now that the Jenkins door is closed, Austin, the Todd door may be opening for us." In this belief, Sue lost no time in taking Mabel Loomis Todd under her wing.

Because gossip about Emily was commonplace in Amherst, we thought it best to give our new friend a chance to judge for herself "the strange Emily Dickinson" who wrote poetry, dressed in white, and never left her father's grounds. And so, early in their friendship, Sue showed young Mrs. Todd some of Emily's poems. This was the first step on the road that eventually led to Mrs. Todd editing Emily's poems for publication after Emily was gone.

"Mrs. Todd thinks them remarkable," Sue reported. "Thinks them stronger than any poems recently published, including those by Helen Hunt Jackson. Mrs. Todd is interested in writing herself, Austin. The work she's already done on a novelette makes her appreciate Emily's gift for words. She calls it genius and says the poems should be published by all means."

I laughed. "She doesn't know Emily."

A few days later Sue said that she had talked to Emily about Mrs. Todd and her enthusiastic comment on the poems. "I received a pebble in exchange," teased Sue.

"Why a pebble?"

Sue handed me a slip of paper, and a glance at the first line answered my question. I smiled as I read:

> How happy is the little Stone
> That rambles in the Road alone—
> And doesn't care about careers
> And Exigencies never fears—
> Whose Coat of elemental Brown
> A passing Universe put on
> And independent as the Sun

Associates or glows alone—
Fulfilling absolute Decree
In casual simplicity—

I looked up. "Emily hasn't changed her mind about publication, has she? I envy her her ability to fulfill absolute decree in such casual simplicity. You must show the poem to Mrs. Todd, Sue, as a most fitting introduction to Emily."

I brought Mrs. Todd to the mansion one evening, and she met Vinnie. Our guest being an accomplished musician, Vinnie urged her to try Emily's piano that had long stood silent in the parlor, except when occasional friends came to play. Mrs. Todd was soon filling the house with her playing and singing.

I knew that Mother would be listening in her room upstairs, and I suspected that Emily would tiptoe down to stand in the shadows of the hallway so as not to miss a note or a word.

"I seem to *feel* your sister," Mrs. Todd whispered, "though I cannot see her."

Soon Maggie came with glasses of sherry and a few lines from Emily for Mrs. Todd. I could see our guest's face light up as she deciphered the words:

Elysium is as far as to
The very nearest Room . . .

"It's one of the greatest compliments I've ever had!" she exclaimed. "I must think of something in return. Has your sister a favorite flower, Mr. Dickinson?"

I had to smile. "All flowers are her favorites. Arbutus
. . . pink orchis . . . heliotrop . . . cape jasmin. Anything
you might mention."

"Indian pipe?"

"One of her most favorite."

"Your sister reminds me of Indian pipe . . . she's so
white and unexpected. When I am at my mother's in
Washington next week, I shall paint white Indian pipes
on a black panel and send them to her."

Later Mrs. Todd told me with elation of a note
Emily had sent in gratitude for the Indian pipes. "She
says it seemed almost supernatural for me to send them;
to her they are the preferred flowers of life."

Mrs. Todd's happiness overflowed the cup a few
weeks later when she received a line from Emily saying
that she could not make an Indian pipe but would Mrs.
Todd please accept a hummingbird? Mrs. Todd read
me the poem.

> A Route of Evanesence
> With a revolving Wheel—
> A Resonance of Emerald—
> A Rush of Cochineal—
> And every Blossom on the Bush
> Adjusts its tumbled Head—
> The mail from Tunis probably,
> An easy Morning's Ride—

It struck me as being one of Emily's best poems. It
brought back the many times we had stood watching a
hummingbird in her garden as it vibrated over a blossom

before thrusting its eager beak into the honey cup.

"She can transfix a hummingbird into a very small compass," I commented.

"Nobody else could do it so well," Mrs. Todd replied, her face bright with admiration. "Nobody else."

CHAPTER 15

Sue was right about another door opening for us. The Todds added zest to our lives, and for a time they brought us closer, as the Jenkins had done.

Within a few months Mrs. Todd proposed an activity that intrigued Sue. A dramatic and vivid story by Frances Hodgson Burnett had been running serially in *Scribner's Monthly*. Emily had been amused by the avidity with which the young people of the neighborhood borrowed her copies of the magazine as the installments of *A Fair Barbarian* came out. Sue was all eagerness when Mrs. Todd suggested that they stage a performance of a dramatized version of the story while interest was running high.

Sue had an important role, of course, and Mattie and Ned and Gilbert each played a part. Mrs. Todd played the leading lady. I wondered how that was going to set with Sue, accustomed as she was to being the leading lady. But if she felt any resentment, she kept it under control, and the play turned out to be a great success.

The Todds added a grace note to all our lives during what turned out to be a year of sorrow for us Dickinsons. Within two months of their coming, Dr. Holland died suddenly, and we had to face the wrench of losing another old friend. Then came a tragic loss for Emily. Vinnie learned of it first when her eye fell on a news item in the *Republican*. Dr. Wadsworth had died suddenly of pneumonia in Philadelphia. Vinnie ran to tell Emily.

"And what did Emily say?" I asked.

"She couldn't believe it at first. Then she said, 'How *can* the sun shine, Vinnie?' And she hasn't mentioned his name since."

My heart went out to Emily. It was much harder for her to lose old friends than for the rest of us who kept making new friends through the church and the College and on occasional trips away from home. Her list of old friends was growing shorter and shorter, and her secluded life kept her from making new ones. Yet somehow she found the strength to stand alone.

A month after Dr. Wadsworth's death, Judge Lord was stricken suddenly and his life was despaired of. It seemed impossible. Just two weeks before, he had made us a visit, in his usual buoyant health and high spirits.

When the news came, Emily was writing him a letter.

"She grasped at the arms of her chair to keep from falling," Vinnie told me. "I ran to her, and she was as cold as ice. She said her sight slipped at the news, Austin."

A few days later I was glad to bring a reassuring report that the Judge was slowly rallying.

"Then Emily can finish her letter to him!" Vinnie exclaimed. "She wanted to send him heliotropes, his favorite flower, but feared the trip to Salem would wilt them. Nothing can wilt her letter."

One sorrow followed another that year of '82. In July our good old friend and neighbor, Luke Sweetser, died, followed soon after by his wife. And in November . . .

On the morning of the fourteenth Vinnie sent Maggie to fetch me. "It's your mother, Mr. Austin. She had a restless night. We got her lifted out of bed to her chair earlier than customary. She said to Miss Vinnie not to leave her. 'Twas the last words she ever spoke." Big, kindly Maggie lifted the corner of her apron to wipe her eyes.

I found Emily in the kitchen, warming herself at the stove after the chilling reality of Mother's death.

"To think," she said, "that the one who could not walk has *flown*, Austin—as ably as a bird! Where has she gone?"

Emily had asked the same question about Father,

time and again. Where had he gone? How small and pale she looked, standing there by the big stove?

"A larger mother died than had she died before," she murmured.

"Now you and Vinnie must take a long rest," I urged, "before you collapse."

"Especially Vinnie, Austin. She's been the ant and the bee and the beaver. I've just done the butterfly part."

"You both did everything you could for Mother, and your devotion never wore thin under the strain."

"Her little wants," Emily mused. "Each so little and yet they consumed the time—reading to her, fanning her, telling her she would be better tomorrow."

"Your own books went unopened," I said accusingly.

"No, not entirely. I got so I snatched a line at a time for myself, taking it with me to the kitchen, then going back for another. But Mother achieved dimension in her illness, and that made up for everything."

After the funeral Vinne took to her bed, utterly exhausted. "Now nothing else can happen," she said. "Nothing!"

Strange, how certain pictures and phrases stay with us, to be picked up again at some later time and fitted into another context. I had never forgotten something Emily said one hazy September day a few years after Father died. I was helping move some of the heavier plants from the west porch to the conservatory for the winter. I knew Emily was referring to the change from summer to autumn when she said suddenly, "We go to sleep with the peach in our hands, Austin, and awake

222

with the stone." But it struck me at the time that the metaphor applied to life as well.

Before the year 1883 was over, Sue and I and Emily and Vin awoke to find the bitterest stone of all in our hands, the peach irretrievably gone.

The year began like any other, with the usual ups and downs of work and pleasure, hopes and disappointments. Emily and Vin were spending a cold and quiet winter trying to regain their strength under Maggie's solicitous care. In January I got away for a few relaxed days with the Jenkinses in Pittsfield. When I returned, I thought I detected strained relations between Sue and Mabel Todd, but Mattie continued to take piano lessons from Mrs. Todd; so I hoped I was wrong.

In March, Sue and Mattie took a trip to New York, and as soon as they returned, Sue planned a sugaring-off party at Sunderland. We drove away with a jangling of sleigh bells and a gaiety of singing as in the old days. I could picture Emily at her window, looking up from her book and listening, happy for our fun and happy, too, for her solitude.

Solitude? Hardly that, for books and thoughts were her companions. Once I found her reading the *Life of Emily Brontë* with such absorption that she didn't hear me enter the room. With a start she said, "Oh, Austin, you must read this. It has so strange a strength. Nothing has been so electric to me since *Jane Eyre*, and you know what that meant to both of us."

I knew, too, what the novels of George Eliot and the poetry of Elizabeth Barrett Browning had meant.

By mid-summer I no longer had any doubt about Sue's feeling of resentment and jealousy toward Mabel Loomis Todd. We made no more joint visits to the Todds' house, but my affection for them continued unabated. When Sue found that I would not give ground on this, she yielded gracefully for the time being, and we resumed the joint visits that had once meant so much to us. Something was missing, though, and never found again, something that in time ate away the last vestige of understanding between Sue and Mabel Todd.

Late in the summer Judge Lord and his two nieces came to Amherst for a visit. Emily fluttered about in expectation. "I have been polishing Mr. Shakespeare," she told me. "I wouldn't like for the Judge to find him rusty."

The day after Judge Lord's arrival, Ned came down with an acute attack that seemed to affect his heart. Now in his early twenties, a student at the College, he was still subject to recurrent illnesses. I sent Gib over to the mansion to tell Emily what had happened.

It was a mild night for September, and we had Ned in the downstairs bedroom with the windows open. The fragrance of the big sweetbrier rosebush wafted into the room. As the night wore on, it grew cool, and Mattie went to close the windows. I thought I heard her talking to someone but, looking up, I could see no one.

She came to me, breathless. "Aunt Emily was standing there, Papa."

"Aunt Emily! Where?"

"By the rosebush. She whispered, 'Is he better, Mattie? Is he better?' And when I told her he was perhaps a little better, she was gone."

In a few days Ned was talking about a new tennis racquet, and we all breathed more easily.

That was a beautiful September. The excitement I always felt as a child in the fall when the leaves began to turn never left me. It meant the coming of Cattle Show day, the finest holiday in the year for Amherst. It meant a special fragrance in the air, and a haze that turned the Holyoke range and the faraway Berkshires to misty blue. Emily never quite agreed with me about the glories of fall. To her, September meant putting stoves back in the house and storm windows on. It meant that the long Massachusetts winter she dreaded was about to set in.

On the next to the last day of September, Gib came down with a high fever. He hadn't been feeling well for a few days, but none of us expected him to have an illness that amounted to anything. Now the doctor feared it might be an attack of typhoid-malarial fever. I looked at the flushed face on the pillow.

Almost beside myself with anxiety, I asked Sue, "How could Gib get typhoid-malarial fever?"

"I don't know, Austin. All I know is that he came home muddy and wet a week or so ago. He was playing with Kendall Emerson in a mudhole, and he fell in. I didn't say anything about it because you've warned him about mudholes so many times."

Sue and I sat up with Gib all that night, trying to

225

ease the fever, trying to make him comfortable. He was so young, just eight years old—and so indispensable. I couldn't imagine life without him. Tears stung my face, though I tried to hold them back.

During the night Vinnie came with Maggie, begging to relieve us at the bedside so we could get some sleep.

"Emily says to tell you that hope never knew horizon," Vinnie said. "It is the bird in the soul that never stops singing."

On the day the crisis was due, Sue and I hardly moved from Gib's side. Mrs. Todd and other friends came to inquire, but we couldn't bear to see them. That night we were startled to have Emily come across the drying grass with Maggie—the first time Emily had been in our house for many years. The odor of disinfectants hung heavy in the room, and I saw her gasp for breath as she came in. She put a single bright flower in my hand. "But he gathered hearts, not flowers," she whispered.

Gib stirred and mumbled something. We strained to hear. Then in a clear voice he cried out in delirium, "Open the door! Open the door! They are waiting for me."

I looked at Emily, and she tiptoed to my side. "What does he mean?" I whispered. "Who's waiting for him?"

She answered, "All that I have, I would give to know."

By three o'clock in the morning Emily had become so sickened by anxiety and the disinfectants that she had to leave.

That afternoon . . . Gib died.

The light went out of my life. I felt a great weariness creeping into my bones, a wild fever burning in my head. I went to bed wracked with an attack of malaria. Oh, not just malaria, I knew well enough. I hardly cared if the doctor and Sue could pull me through. In my delirium I was constantly with Gib, chasing fireflies with him, taking him to task for playing in mudholes, smiling as he urged my high-stepping horse to race down the Sunderland road.

Emily collapsed after that night in the sickroom, but I didn't know about it until later. In a few weeks she had recovered enough to send messages to Sue. Sue came to my bed during one of my rational spells, and I saw that she had been weeping. In a husky voice she asked if I could listen to some of Emily's words. I nodded. This was the Sue I had lost so often and only occasionally found again. This was the Sue I had loved before we drifted apart. I reached for her hand, and we looked at each other through blurred eyes.

"Perhaps we loved him too much," she said.

I could find no words for an answer.

"Emily says she sees him in the star. She meets his velocity in everything that flies. She says his life was like the bugle . . ."

"Yes, yes."

"She sent us a few poems, Austin. I can't read them today. But these four lines are for you to dream over:

Pass to thy Rendezvous of Light,
Pangless except for us—
Who slowly ford the Mystery
Which thou hast leaped across!

"Oh, Sue," I cried, turning my face to the wall, "why did he have to leap so fast?"

Without Emily to stir our spirits in those first dreadful weeks after Gib's death, life would have been without a single shaft of sun. She sent us philosophy. She sent us wisdom. She sent us glimpses into eternity. Through her grief she found a way to a height Sue and I could not reach. We both knew that Emily's heart was torn by Gib's death. She had delighted in him every day of his life. But she was learning to fly again . . .

One day Sue brought to my bedside a copy of the Amherst paper. "I don't know if I can read it, Austin," she said when I awoke at teatime, clear in my mind. "It's about Gib."

"I don't know if I can listen," I answered.

She choked. "They call it *Death of a Promising Boy*." I could feel my fever rising.

"Though he was only eight years old," Sue read, "we are astonished to find how many people Gilbert interested. Intuitively he found the real stuff of humanity beneath all kinds of garbs and in the old as well as the young . . ." Sue could go no further. We clutched at each other like children.

By December I was on my feet again. I ventured out to the stable to see how the horses were faring.

There, standing against the wall inside the door, was Gib's sled, alone in the cold. I leaned against the wall, alone in the cold, too.

As Christmas approached, I knew how Emily would be remembering . . . when she prepared the usual gifts and notes for friends and neighbors. I walked over one afternoon and sat in the kitchen with Vinnie while she cut up fruit for the holiday baking. Emily was busy in her room. On the old kitchen table, neatly wrapped and ready to be delivered, lay packages and jars and boxes. I picked up a card and read in Emily's handwriting, "Santa Claus comes with a Smile and a Tear."

"He won't come to me at all any more," I mumbled.

I looked at some of the parcels. One was for the Jameson boy, who had often played with Gib. "Gilbert's little Mates are still dear to his Aunt Emily," the card read. And for Kendall Emerson, the boy who had played with Gib at the mudhole, there was a Christmas wreath with the message: "Santa Claus still asks the way to Gilbert's little friends—Is Heaven an unfamiliar Road?"

I bowed my head. Yes, for me Heaven was an unfamiliar road. Perhaps Emily's way was best—to live with thoughts instead of trying to put them out of one's head, to companion with eternity. I rubbed my coat sleeve across my eyes and waited to speak until I was sure I could control my voice. Thinking about Father sometimes helped when I was wracked by emotion. "Don't wear your feelings on your sleeve, Austin," he used to say.

In a few minutes I managed to say, "Christmas should be a time of joy, Vinnie. But I've forgotten what joy is."

Vinnie's only reply was a choking sound.

I stumbled across the snow-packed path toward home. Chickadees were busy in the pines, twittering merrily. How many years ago was it that Emily told me about Father feeding the birds? How he slipped behind the door, so as not to embarrass them. I went to the stable and shoveled a wide place in front of the door and threw out a full measure of chicken feed for the birds. Standing back in the shadow of the doorway, I watched them swoop down, full of life and eagerness. I must ask Emily, I thought, why heaven isn't an unfamiliar road for her.

CHAPTER *16*

EMILY's exhaustion after Gib's death was physical. Mine was both physical and of the spirit. Although Emily never fully regained her health, her spirit soon rose above the bondage of illness. Even during those first months of acute loss and suffering she had a certain sense of joy in living. Rarely did she cease to believe that we underrate our chance to dwell on this "matchless earth." She said to me at this time, "Take all away from me but leave me ecstasy, and I have all."

As I recovered from the attack of malaria, I walked in a fog of depression that refused to lift. I knew I had to go on with the routine of living. Numbly I went to the office. Numbly I carried out my duties as treasurer of the college and acted as moderator at town meeting. But behind the façade of activity, my life was hollow. With Emily there was no façade, only substance.

She tried to assure me that time was the great healer. I remember one stormy evening when I talked with her in her room. Nervous exhaustion kept her confined to bed for weeks at a time that fall and winter. She was propped up with pillows, her ever-present pencil and books beside her. The light from her lamp and the flickering flames from her Franklin stove gave the big room a comforting glow. Her four window sills were bright with plants, mostly hyacinths, which she coaxed into bloom while winter still buried the garden under two feet of snow.

We had been talking about Gib, Emily telling me how he had always rejoiced in secrets. "He always wanted at least one secret with me," she said. "A dozen were better. His life was panting with secrets. 'Don't tell, Aunt Emily! Don't tell!' And now, Austin, he has a secret from *me*. From *us*. Now he knows a way that to us is still a mystery. Now he can instruct us."

"But how?"

"That is part of the secret."

It took a long time for me to glimpse any of the light that Emily had assured me would follow the darkness. More than once I despaired in that bleak fall and winter of 1883-84, much as I tried to keep my mind off my sorrow. The night Matthew Arnold lectured in Amherst, I went to College Hall with Ned, vowing to take careful note of everything the great English poet had to say so that I could report to Emily. She was so eager to hear. But my mind wandered woefully, and poor Emily had to rely on the account in the paper with little contribution from me.

We were just beginning to get adjusted to life without Gib when the next blow came. Before spring broke the gloom of winter, Judge Lord suffered a stroke. Two days later he died.

I felt concern for Emily. She would miss Judge Lord more than the rest of us would, especially if there was a grain of truth in that story Sue told me the day I didn't want to listen. What *was* Emily's feeling for Judge Lord? For years they had corresponded, exchanging ideas and even amusing newspaper clippings. Theirs was a deep and meaningful friendship. Whether it was more than that no one knew, except perhaps Vin and she would never tell.

One of the nieces wrote from Salem that the last words of a note Judge Lord was writing when he was stricken were, "A caller comes."

With a catch in her throat Emily said, "It must have been Eternity. He never came back."

Vinnie told me that for a few days Emily found it hard to reconcile herself to the loss of another loved friend. But as she thought of eternity, the sea parting to show a further sea, and that a further, her peace of mind returned.

"Each that we lose takes part of us," she told Vin. "It's like the tide pulling at the moon. I am only a crescent now over the eternal sea."

Only a crescent . . . and what a frail crescent physically! But in my eyes Emily continued to be at the full, mentally and spiritually.

Although tired and worn, she spent a great deal of her time writing her incomparable letters—to Mrs. Holland, to our Norcross cousins, to Colonel Higginson, to Sue, to Helen Hunt Jackson, and to others. And poems? No one knew if she was writing any, and no one knew how many she had written down the years . . . not until later when Vinnie discovered hundreds and hundreds of them in a drawer of Emily's cherry bureau. Sue guessed that Emily was finding solace in putting down her thoughts in poetry, and two weeks after Judge Lord's death, Sue felt her supposition justified when a note came from Emily with a poem. I carried the first two lines around with me for weeks:

'Tis not the swaying frame we miss,
It is the steadfast Heart

A procession of months crept by, and still time proved to be a reluctant healer. Mattie went off to school. Sue became active again in social affairs. Ned continued his studies at the College. There was no Gib to fly down the walk to greet me when I came home from the office. I found it impossible to shake off my depression. Often I sought refuge at the mansion; often I found a measure of peace at the Todds', listening to Mrs. Todd play and sing. But the spark had gone from life.

For a while Emily's health seemed to improve. She could be downstairs, tending to her plants again. Then one June morning Stephen, the boy at the barn, appeared at my office in a great state of excitement.

"It's Miss Emily, Squire. She's fainted dead away. Miss Vinnie says she's never fainted before and wants you to come quick."

I hurried to the homestead.

Emily had been in the kitchen making a cake with Maggie when darkness engulfed her and she lost consciousness. We hovered over her all day . . . the doctor and Vin, and Sue and I. Not until late at night did she return to us.

"I thought I had died," she said when she opened her eyes. "Everything was so hallowed."

There seemed no end to calamities. In August we read in the *Republican* that Helen Hunt Jackson had fallen downstairs at her home in Colorado Springs and broken her leg in three places. It was a serious accident. Emily wrote to her at once, though she herself was confined to bed and chair.

Helen's reputation had been growing with the years. Her most recent book, *Ramona*, with an American-Indian background, was achieving renown. Critics were calling it her best. I felt awe and gratitude that this much-published writer should think so highly of Emily's poems.

Emily showed me the answer she received from Helen of Colorado. Her leg was healing, and she was already on crutches. Farther down the page I saw that Helen was still urging Emily to allow her poems to be published.

"I've just finished Helen's *Ramona*," Emily said one day. "Pity me, Austin. I wanted it to last forever."

"Mrs. Todd is planning to send over another book for you to read, one she thinks singularly good," I answered. "It's *Called Back*, by Hugh Conway."

Emily found *Called Back* a haunting story. "As our dear Mr. Bowles would say," she told me, "it was greatly impressive to me."

Emily's health went up and down like the weather. Now and then she would feel well enough to be downstairs doing what she could to help with the work. I sometimes feared that, in an effort to spare Vin and Maggie, she went beyond her strength.

I always tried to get over to the homestead late Sunday afternoon to see how things were going. Sunday was a hard day for Vin, with Maggie off visiting her relatives. One Sunday in mid-October, 1884, about five o'clock, I found Vinnie working desperately over Emily. She had had another fainting spell. Feeling somewhat better that day, she had come downstairs to help with dinner preparations. Then she insisted on drying the dishes for Vin. It was too much. Poor frantic Vinnie was unable to move Emily when she fainted and dared not leave her to run to the Evergreens for help.

Health might come and health might go, but Emily's sense of humor remained constant. A month or so after her second bad turn, she was sending me a Thanksgiving message in the form of a resolution giving the thanks of the audience to Mr. Dickinson for his interesting and able turkey. Later she and Vin sent us roasting hens, and Emily's note tied to the gift described them as the birds that don't go south. And then there was the time an epidemic of burglaries struck Amherst. Several houses were burglarized in quick succession, including the Evergreens. About a hundred dollars' worth of Sue's jewelry was stolen and some money from Ned's pocketbook. The loss brought a little note from Emily asking Ned if it was quite safe to leave the Golden Rule out over night.

Helen Hunt Jackson died suddenly in the summer of 1885. She was only fifty-four, only two months older than Emily. Another pull of the tides at the crescent!

By mid-November Emily was so seriously ill that I dared not leave Amherst. Vinnie was beside herself with anxiety. The doctors, after diagnosing the malady as Bright's disease, seemed unable to find a cure.

Though her strength was ebbing month by month, Emily kept in close touch with happenings around her. She wanted to hear all about Sue's trip to New York with Ned after Christmas. She followed Mattie's progress in school at Farmington. She encouraged Ned's interest in working at the College library. She kept abreast of my continuing plans for improving the campus and the streets of Amherst. And, through Vin and Maggie, she followed the activities of our friends and neighbors.

One evening in early 1886 she seemed particularly weak when I visited her. Yet she had a little note ready for Sue in the bowl in which Sue had sent over broth: "Thank you, dear Sue—for every solace."

March had always been an exciting month for Emily. Spring would soon be sidling in to take the place of the long cold New England winter. But when March, 1886, came, I feared it would be the last time Emily would welcome her favorite month.

In April I brought her the first trailing arbutus from the Pelham woods, knowing how she loved it. I brought the first hepatica, a few stems of blossoms before the leaves appeared. How life had changed from the days when Emily and I found the first flowers of spring together!

Emily watched from her window that spring as the snow melted and the buds broke and the grass turned from dun to green. Often in the evening I went over to sit with her. It didn't matter if we talked much or not. Sometimes I read the paper to her. I remember on the evening of my 57th birthday in mid-April I was reading aloud from the *Republican* when my eye caught an item about the book Mrs. Todd had lent Emily. *Called Back* had been made into a play and was running at the Opera House in Springfield.

"Called back . . . ," Emily repeated slowly.

Easter Day was beautiful that year . . . the sky a sea of blue, the sun a cymbal of gold. Violets bloomed in the damp shade near the lilac bushes. I took a bouquet of them to Emily before going to church, and she thanked me for the resurrection.

Before I started for the office on the morning of May 13th, Vinnie sent for me. Emily was very ill, breathing heavily. About ten o'clock she drifted into unconsciousness. Dr. Bigelow spent most of the afternoon with her, but he was unable to rouse her enough to get her to take his medicine.

All the next day there was no change. I had the awful feeling that Emily would not awaken again on this side. The thought choked me. I told Vin I had to go out for a breath of air.

"Here, Austin, take this. Put it in an envelope and mail it." She handed me a piece of paper. "I found it in the Brontë book this morning. It's Emily's last let-ter . . . to Fanny and Loo."

As I folded the white sheet, I couldn't help seeing the five words scrawled on it.

<blockquote>
"Little Cousins,
Called Back.
Emily."
</blockquote>

I hurried from the room. *Called Back* . . . those two ringing words brought me the assurance that Emily had no doubt about immortality as she felt her life slipping away. Called back . . . to Gib, to Father, to Mother, to Judge Lord, to Samuel Bowles . . . to the eternity she spoke of so often. Called back . . . to fathom the secret Gib was keeping for us.

Early the next evening, on the 15th of May, 1886, Emily died without regaining consciousness.

Vinnie was on the point of collapse. I was too de-presed to think. We left all the funeral arrangements to Sue, confident that she would know what would please Emily.

"How can I live without her? How can I live without her?" she kept crying. One of the reasons neither ever married, I often thought, was that marrying would have meant being separated. Vinnie's cry came from the depths of her heart, and it found an echo in mine. "How can I live without her?"

Sue wrote the obituary notice for the *Springfield Republican,* and it was printed on the editorial page. How well Sue said it! As I read, certain words and phrases stood out like the Pelham hills: "her sensitive nature . . . endowments so exceptional . . . her talk and writings were like no one's else . . . her intimate and passionate love of nature . . . she seized the kernel instantly . . ."

For flowers Sue chose the simplest. "Remember, Austin, that first Memorial Day after Gib left us? Emily chose lilies of the valley for Gib, and Damson-plum blossoms and hawthorn for your Father and Mother. And remember what she said about herself? 'When it shall come my turn, I want a Buttercup.'"

"I'll bring some from the meadow."

"And violets and ground pine and apple blossoms, Austin. And a handful of pansies, and lilies of the valley for the piano."

I was bringing apple blossoms into the parlor when Vinnie came with two heliotropes. "These are to be put by Emily's hand," she said.

"Heliotropes?" It seemed to me they would be out of place with the other flowers. "Why heliotropes, Vin?"

"For Emily to take to Judge Lord," Vinnie whispered. I looked after her as she tiptoed away. For Judge

Lord! Not to take to Father, or Mother, or Gib . . . but to Judge Lord. A warm feeling of gratitude stole over me. It had seemed to be Emily's fate to pour herself out, always to pour herself out. But this time, perhaps there had been a return.

It was a beautiful afternoon, the day we laid Emily to rest, the kind of afternoon she would have gloried in. Morning had awakened a little dull and hazy, but by afternoon dazzling sunlight brightened the fields and glittered on the young leaves. Jonathan Jenkins came from Pittsfield to say a prayer. Colonel Higginson came from Cambridge to speak a few words before reading Emily Brontë's poem on immortality, which our Emily loved above all others, the poem with those two powerful final stanzas:

> Though earth and man were gone,
> And suns and universes cease to be,
> And Thou wert left alone,
> Every existence would exist in Thee.
>
> There is not room for Death,
> Nor atom that his might could render void:
> Thou—Thou art Being and Breath,
> And what Thou art may never be destroyed.

Not room for death . . . what did it mean? I had no Emily now to turn to, to ask. And yet I knew what she would have answered. "Only of the body, Austin. Death only of the body. Not an atom of the essence."

Many of the old friends from the College were there

for the funeral. Six of them acted as honorary pallbearers and carried the small white casket out of the rear door at the end of the hall. There six of the old faithfuls took over, men who had worked on the grounds and in the stable, men Emily felt were her friends. Gently they carried her across the fields to the cemetery. Had Emily told Sue this was what she wanted?

We followed—across the lawn, through the hedge, through fields sparkling with Emily's buttercups, along ferny paths. It wasn't far. As we passed behind the old Pleasant Street house, I thought how surprised Emily would be to see the pine grove, grown so tall and handsome in the years since she had watched its progress.

How simple it all was; how beautiful in the May sunlight! Birds sang . . . Emily's bluebirds and robins. One of her bobolinks called. One of her hummingbirds whizzed by on its route of evanescence. Apple trees bloomed in the orchards, and the perfume of spring filled the air. On such a day there did indeed seem to be no room for death. Emily would have read these bulletins of spring with delight. But now, I reminded myself, she was interested in other news . . . the first-hand news of immortality.

POSTSCRIPT

FOR THOSE who may be curious to know what happened after Emily Dickinson's death, here in brief is the story.

Austin's marriage endured, with continuing ups and downs, until his death in 1895, nine years after Emily's death. To the end he was active in College and town affairs.

Ned survived his father by less than three years. Always plagued by ill health, Ned lived at home and never married.

Vinnie lived on at the homestead for the remaining thirteen years of her life, with faithful Maggie to help with the work.

Sue continued to be active in social affairs for many years, and did not die until 1913 in her eighty-third year.

In 1903 Martha (Mattie) married Alexander Bianchi. She died childless forty years later, and with her death the Dickinson line came to an end. But Emily's poems continued to live and to become more and more well-known and appreciated as the years passed.

When Vinnie discovered dozens of little packets of

Emily's poems after her death, she was amazed. Although she knew that Emily had written poetry for years, she had no conception of the quantity of her output. Eager that the poems be published as soon as possible to establish Emily's reputation as a poet, Vinnie urged Sue to get the poems in shape for publication. Sue dallied for months without making a decision. Finally Vinnie recovered the poems and pleaded with Mrs. Todd to edit them in cooperation with Col. Higginson. Finally in 1890 and 1891 the first two small volumes of Emily Dickinson's poems, edited by Mrs. Todd and Colonel Higginson, were published.

The success of the poems and the interest stimulated in the poet prompted Austin, Lavinia, and Mrs. Todd to collect letters Emily had written to friends and relatives. Mrs. Todd edited them for publication and two volumes of the letters appeared in 1894.

From time to time after that additional volumes of poems and letters appeared, edited by Mrs. Todd, by her daughter Millicent Todd Bingham, and by Martha Dickinson Bianchi. But it was not until the 1950's that the whole body of Emily Dickinson's work was collected and published in two complete sets of 1775 poems and 1049 letters, arranged as far as could be determined according to the date when they were written. These sets, three volumes of the poems and three volumes of the letters, were edited and annotated by Thomas H. Johnson, a painstaking task to which he devoted many years.

A.F. & O.R.

BIBLIOGRAPHY

ANDERSON, CHARLES R. *Emily Dickinson's Poetry; Stairway of Surprise.* New York: Holt, Rinehart & Winston, 1960.

BIANCHI, MARTHA DICKINSON. *Emily Dickinson Face to Face.* Boston: Houghton Mifflin, 1932.

———. *The Life and Letters of Emily Dickinson.* Boston: Houghton Mifflin Company, 1924.

BINGHAM, MILLICENT TODD. *Emily Dickinson—A Revelation.* New York: Harper, 1954.

———. *Emily Dickinson's Home.* New York: Harper, 1955.

CHASE, RICHARD VOLNEY. *Emily Dickinson.* New York: William Sloane Associates, 1951.

245

JOHNSON, THOMAS H., ed. *The Poems of Emily Dickinson.* 3 vols. Cambridge, Mass.: The Belknap Press of Harvard University Press, 1958.

———. *Emily Dickinson; An Interpretive Biography.* Cambridge, Mass.: The Belknap Press of Harvard University Press, 1955.

JOHNSON, THOMAS H. and THEODORA WARD, eds. *The Letters of Emily Dickinson.* 3 vols. Cambridge, Mass.: The Belknap Press of Harvard University Press, 1958.

LEYDA, JAY. *The Years and Hours of Emily Dickinson.* 2 vols. New Haven: The Yale University Press, 1960.

WARD, THEODORA. *The Capsule of the Mind: Chapters in the Life of Emily Dickinson.* Cambridge, Mass.: The Belknap Press of Harvard University Press, 1961.

WELLS, HENRY W. *Introduction to Emily Dickinson.* Chicago: Hendricks House, 1947.

WHICHER, GEORGE FRISBIE. *This Was a Poet.* New York: Charles Scribner's Sons, 1938.